CW00554459

The Larry Diaries

The Larry Diaries

*Downing Street: The First 100 Days
as Chief Rat-Catcher*

**SIMON &
SCHUSTER**

London · New York · Sydney · Toronto · New Delhi

A CBS COMPANY

First published in Great Britain by Simon & Schuster UK Ltd, 2011
A CBS COMPANY

1 3 5 7 9 10 8 6 4 2

Simon & Schuster UK Ltd
1st Floor
222 Gray's Inn Road
London WC1X 8HB

www.simonandschuster.co.uk

Simon & Schuster Australia, Sydney
Simon & Schuster India, New Delhi

A CIP catalogue record for this book is available
from the British Library.

ISBN: 978-0-85720-763-0

Printed in Great Britain by CPI Group (UK) Ltd, Croydon, CR0 4YY

FEBRUARY 2011

Tuesday 15 February 2011

Listen, I was nervous, OK?

One minute I was in Battersea Dogs & Cats Home, shacked up with a load of reprobates and misfits; the next thing I know I'm at No 10 Downing Street, behind the big black door, meeting the Prime Minister and all his staff, and being briefed on my new role as 'chief mouser to the cabinet office'. In other words, I'm the new rodent bouncer in the gaff.

Since the last minder got his marching orders it's been open season for every gate-crashing *rattus norvegicus* this side of the river who wants to squat at London's most famous address. Truth be told, they might have got away with it if they'd kept their pointy little heads down, but streaking across the front porch on live telly was, frankly, taking liberties.

Of course, it wasn't a good look for Dave and Sam to have vermin running around their front door – not with all those visiting dignitaries coming and going – so someone from No 10 was on the blower sharpish to Battersea after that, and yours truly was hauled from his bed and given the once over. Apparently, the chief handler down there had seen me getting my claws into one of the squeaky fellas and decided I was the home's 'most promising rat-catcher'. Quite an accolade.

Don't get me wrong; I'm not saying I can't handle the job. This could be the moment my luck turns after a bit of a sticky patch. But the first thing I did when I got here was search for a way out. They thought I was making a break for it, but I was merely checking the exits as a precaution. Let's just say it's a habit I've picked up over the years.

When they hauled me out to meet that lot out front – the scribblers and the snappers – I admit it, the old red mist came down. You can't know what it's like to have all those microphones and cameras shoved in your whiskers until you've experienced it. Put it this way, the next time some celeb clobbers a paparazzo I'll be cheering him on.

Then that bird from *ITV News* grabbed me and stuck me on her lap. It's nothing personal, but I felt that was a bit previous, and since I didn't know what was happening, I gave her a little scratch – just to let her know I'm no pushover. Sorry, love. Still, it's not done my reputation any harm.

But you don't get something for nothing these days, and now I'm faced with the challenge of having to earn me keep. The thing is, I'm just an average cat who's been plonked down in a swanky address, at least until they realize I'm actually no great shakes at rat-catching and sling me out.

4

So I'm writing all this down. Well, if Tony Blair and Peter Mandelson can do it, why shouldn't I? Haven't I too been on 'The Journey'? And I reckon I've already stumbled across things even they might never have clocked. You see, I'm small enough to crawl into the sort of tight corners those two spent their working lives trying to avoid.

Take this morning. After they let me out of that economy-class travel cage, I ran down to the basement – just to collect my thoughts, nothing more. It was dark, but my eyes adjusted soon enough, and amongst the old filing cabinets and office furniture I could make out a small pile of mobile phones and Blackberries – every one of them smashed to pieces, broken beyond repair.

There were brand new computer monitors alongside them and I swear to you not a single screen was intact.

What sort of place is this? I thought to myself. It's hardly surprising I was edgy by the time they wheeled me out to meet the press.

Later on, after the whole meet-and-greet affair was over, I bumped into the big man himself – David Cameron – wandering down the corridor in his chinos, Kate and Wills wedding mug in hand. He was humming an old tune by The Smiths – 'This Charming Man', I think it was – as if he didn't have a care in the world.

'What's the score with all that smashed up hardware in the basement?' I asked him, straight out.

'It looks like Charlie Sheen's been let loose in the Apple store.'

'Oh, don't worry about that,' Cameron replied, laughing. 'Let's just say the last guy was a bit of a ... problem tenant.'

'I think I'm with you,' I said, nodding. 'Is it too late to hit him with a retrospective ASBO?'

Wednesday 16 February – morning

I've been given a basket in the 'events and meetings' room, where pretty young things organize the PM's diary. It's not exactly luxurious, but it's a big improvement on the cage I was slammed up in down Wandsworth way, and far quieter. Even now, I can still hear the sound of cats squealing and dogs howling. It's a wonder I ever got any kip.

I sleep on a royal wedding cushion with 'William' and 'Kate' embroidered on the front below an image of the happy couple. Another two names – 'John' and 'Lewis' – are stitched into the back. Perhaps they are 'minor royals'? That's the name the events girls give to wannabes who would love to be at Westminster Abbey on the big day but are unlikely to make the cut. It's an austerity wedding, after all, so places are in short supply.

The decor in my place is surprisingly shabby – even

the beige-coloured wallpaper is dog-eared in places — but it's peaceful and the girls make a fuss of me, scratching me under my chin until I purr loudly and sneaking in snacks I can chomp on while they go about their work.

The photocopier in the corner comes in handy as well. When the sun disappears behind Downing Street and the shadows on the shabby carpet have crept to the furthest corners of the room, I hop on there and warm myself up. The events girls tut and shake their heads, but I see them smiling to one another when they think I'm not looking. A log fire would be nice but you work with what you're given, don't you?

I'd say I'm settling in pretty well, only I'm still not allowed to venture out beyond a small suite of rooms. I think they're worried I'll do a runner, but they needn't be — I know when I've landed on my feet!

David Cameron, or 'DC' as I've taken to calling him, had a special visitor this morning. I was perched on the back of a cream sofa on the first-floor landing, peering through one of the windows overlooking Downing Street, when a silver Audi pulled up outside No 10.

Given the make of the motor, I thought that German *fräulein* Angela Merkel had turned up for a tear-up over the EU budget. So imagine my surprise when Prince Charles clambered out.

DC's missus Samantha had left my door ajar so I

slipped through it and raced down the sweeping staircase and through the corridor, which leads to the high-ceilinged reception lobby on the other side of that familiar front door. I curled up under a chair in the corner of the room, making myself comfortable at the very moment Charlie strode in.

I assumed HRH had popped by to discuss wedding plans, only it turns out he wanted to have a natter about trees. Not unexpected for him, when you think about his history chatting to plants and that. It seems he's none too happy about the government's plan to sell off forests to private companies, so they can chop down the trees for a quick profit. Well, it's a bit of a liberty, isn't it? If they were doing the same in Brazil, that bloke out of Coldplay would be going ape. I'm surprised he hasn't been on the dog and bone already.

Charlie seems like a nice enough bloke up close, but the problem is he's not really supposed to stick his nose in, is he? There was a lot of talk around here about 'monstrous carbuncles' before he arrived. I've no idea what a carbuncle is, but a monstrous one sounds pretty unpleasant.

The Prince fires off letters whenever he feels passionate about something, and it turns out he feels passionate most of the time. Architecture, climate change, agriculture – Charles has plenty to say about all of them, and he doesn't just confine his thoughts to the page, either.

A good half a dozen or so ministers have been

summoned to Clarence House for a chat over tea and cucumber sandwiches in the last year, according to DC, and I reckon he has given some of them a right ear-bashing. No one looks forward to those meetings, or so the boss says, and I suspect DC wasn't exactly thrilled when he heard about today's get-together with HRH.

I listened to Charlie ruminating as he strode back and forth across the black-and-white tiled floor in the entrance hall. 'Heir to Blair,' he was repeating, thoughtfully.

'"Heir to Blair", that's what you called yourself, isn't it?' he asked DC.

'I suppose I did, Your Highness, yes.'

'Oh, please, don't bother with any of that titled rubbish, Prime Minister.'

'Right you are, er, Sir . . . and please, call me David.'

'Ah yes, that's what Blair said too, isn't it?'

'What? Call me David?'

'No, call me Tony.'

I didn't have a Scooby-Doo what they were rabbiting on about at this point, I don't mind telling you.

'Well, formalities have their place, but times have changed . . . Charles,' DC was saying.

'Haven't they just,' Charlie continued. 'I was rather fond of Blair. But then we had a little disagreement about fox-hunting, as you might know.'

'Yes, well, we're reversing all that.'

'Indeed, very sensible, but it would be a terrible

9

shame if we fell out over this plan of yours to sell off our ancient woodlands. Could make life rather awkward, eh?'

I tell you what, Charlie's no fool. DC said nothing, but I could tell from his face he knew immediately what HRH was getting at.

And I could see the boss's mind working overtime, thinking about the number of wedding invitations he might be able to squeeze out of Clarence House if he did Charlie a favour. Put it this way, I'd put money on that forest scheme getting the chop.

Wednesday 16 February – afternoon

You've got to hand it to him, he doesn't waste much time.

Sky News was on in the events room this afternoon. It's the only channel they ever seem to watch around here. I was having a doze, but I was rudely interrupted by the chatter of the office types, who'd gathered around the gogglebox to watch DC do his stuff in the House of Commons.

He was sparring with Ed Miliband, the young Labour contender who put one in the eye of his brother in the leadership bid (nasty business that). Miliband asked DC if he was happy with his policy on forests. 'The short answer to that is no,' the PM replied, without missing a beat. That caught young Ed off-guard.

Now, I don't know too much about politics, at least not yet, but I'm not sure Caroline Spelman, the woman DC put in charge of all this stuff last year, will be too chuffed about the boss's pronouncement.

One of those civil servant types who was in the room when Dave handed Spelman the job told me this morning DC had issued her with very specific instructions. 'I'm giving you a very brief brief,' he had told her. 'England may no longer be a particularly pleasant land but at least it's still a green one. For God's sake keep it that way.'

Only the chatter at No 10 is that selling off the forests was all Spelman's idea. She was trying to grease up to Boy George, the youngster in charge of balancing the books, by coming up with a plan to raise some cash in a hurry.

Only now I reckon she's going to be about as popular around here as a seal-clubber at a Greenpeace convention.

Thursday 17 February

Spelman's day of reckoning. I knew it was coming. I just didn't think I'd be there to witness it. The thing is, it's easy to go unnoticed when you're a little fella like me, so I set off down the road to Parliament after my morning snooze.

I sneaked out of the big black door, when the copper stationed out front opened it to take delivery of the fresh flowers that arrive each day to spruce the place up, and trotted down Whitehall in the mid-morning gloom. In less than five minutes I was in the shadow of Big Ben, dodging the grim-faced pedestrians rushing past the tall black railings that encircle the building.

Only I didn't go through the main door at St Stephen's Gate, the one where two scary-looking Old Bill stand guard. I've never really seen eye to eye with coppers and I try to steer clear of them whenever I can.

My old man taught me never to go through the front door when you can sneak around the back instead, so I raced through the car park beneath Big Ben, past the cashpoints by the back of Star Chamber and up the stairs, barely pausing to glance at the statues and oil paintings that line the oak-panelled walls of the House of Commons.

Eventually, after clambering up two more sets of stairs, I found my way to a deserted press gallery. But the absence of any activity reminded me that those scribblers spend more time down the boozer than they do reporting Parliament. Two old blokes in ruffled shirts and long black jackets were standing guard, but they were too busy nattering about the football scores to clock me sneaking past them.

From my vantage point, perched on the end of an uncomfortable wooden bench, I looked down on Spelman in the chamber below, telling MPs that the great end-of-season forest sale had been cancelled.

'Sorry,' she said. 'I got this one wrong.' The Labour lot loved that, shouting and cheering like a load of Chelsea fans at Stamford Bridge. 'U-turn! U-turn!' they shouted. More like a handbrake turn if you ask me – it's less than five months since Spelman announced the sell-off in the first place.

But later, back at base, DC seemed unperturbed.

'Tough day for Caroline,' he reflected, as he straightened his tie in the gold-framed mirror in the lobby, picking a speck of dust off the shoulder of his suit as he prepared to step outside for a quick two-minute TV interview.

'Yes, all that forest stuff was a bit harsh,' I remarked.

'Oh no, I wasn't talking about that.' DC smiled. 'She's just found out she hasn't been invited to the wedding. Invitation must have got . . . lost in the post.'

It's true what they say about politics – it's a rough old game.

Friday 18 February – afternoon

I had my collar felt this afternoon.

I was taking a leisurely stroll around the first-floor

corridors, keeping an eye out for holes in the skirting boards and exploring the cavernous khazi that's tucked away behind the room with the big pillars where DC entertains VIPs. Everyone around here says it's the bathroom the Queen uses on the rare occasions she pops in for a visit. I've no idea if it's true, but the thought of HRH sitting on her Downing Street throne made me feel a bit Tom and Dick if I'm honest, so I disappeared next door.

DC was hosting a bash in the Pillared Room, one of the grandest rooms in the gaff, and the scribblers and snappers were out in force, flitting around the boss like the flies that buzz round my cat bowl.

As I approached, I could see why. Kevin Spacey was stood in the centre of the room with his arm around the PM's shoulder, beaming for the cameras.

You've got to admire his front. It's only a few years since he turned up at Labour's big shindig in Blackpool with Bill Clinton and his old mate Peter Mandelson, bursting into the auditorium like a rock star to rapturous applause. Only now he's batting for the other side, so to speak.

Spacey's an A-lister alright, and he knows it, but you have to give him his due: he was a bit tasty in *The Usual Suspects*. A right motley crew, weren't they, that lot? A bit like the Labour front bench.

I only wanted to see what all the fuss was about, but the second I trotted into the room some dark-haired

Doris* grabbed me by my new blue collar and scooped me up.

I knew better than to give her a scratch after all the commotion I caused last time, so I waited patiently for her to carry me out of the room and plonk me back down on the patterned carpet in the hallway.

I found out later Spacey was in to accept an award. He runs a little theatre south of the river, which converted some disused underground space deep below Waterloo Station into another arts venue. 'It's a long way from Beverly Hills, Spacey,' I thought, 'but fair play to you, mate.'

To be honest I don't like the sound of his new project. It's called the Old Vic Tunnels. Think about it – the place must be crawling with rodents. The trouble is, so's No 10.

Friday 18 February – evening

It never stops around here. An hour after K-Space made his exit, none other than Claudia Schiffer and Kate Moss rolled up!

---

* The young girl who grabbed me is called Harriet, by the way. I've seen her around the place because she works in the events room and, well, it's difficult to ignore her. She's always well turned out in very high heels and rather short skirts, and she seems to have taken a bit of a shine to me. A streetwise young moggie like me doesn't need looking after, but on this occasion I might just make an exception.

The fashion crowd were at No 10 tonight for a party thrown by Mrs C. Sir Stuart Rose, the bloke who runs Marks & Sparks, was here an' all. Well, Sam must be one of their best customers. Sir Stu even had a custom-made M&S dress knocked up for her last year in time for the Tory party conference after all his shops sold out. Sam's got a whole cupboard full of M&S clobber in her cramped little bedroom in the flat upstairs. DC calls it her 'public wardrobe'. Granted, there's another two or three crammed with designer gear – Diane Von Furstenberg, Stella McCartney and the like – but none of that stuff seems to get an outing. Tonight was an exception. Mrs C looked a vision in a designer skirt speckled with stars.

I heard one of the fashionistas telling Sam that Mulberry has made me some sort of tailored coat. Now, a good quality leather collar would be one thing, but a fitted designer jacket? It sounds a bit too, well, French, for my liking – fine for your Siamese or your Persians, but not something I'd climb into. Don't get me wrong: I'm not too proud to pimp myself out for PR purposes, but if I'm offered freebies I'd rather earn them – and if I'm going to acquire some sort of celebrity status I'd like to be famous for performing a public service.

But I have to admit I was having fun tonight, and towards the end of the evening I was about to make a beeline for Kate Moss herself. Well, at the end of the day she's just a Croydon girl, ain't she, so why wouldn't the two of us hit it off?

Only then I caught a glimpse of one of those flaming rats, leaning up against the leg of the temporary champagne bar and chewing on a crudité that Anna Wintour had dropped on the floor. I didn't want to cause a scene so I decided to abandon the catwalk and sashay back to my living quarters to ponder the day's events from the safety of my Wills and Kate cushion. I've got some cogitating to do.

Saturday 19 February

I saw DC in his brand-spanking-new kitchen this morning, making a brew in his Kate and Wills mug. I was worried he'd have a pop at me for gate-crashing yesterday's bash, so I started to talk about something else before he could open his trap.

'I just don't understand all this "Big Society" stuff you've been banging on about, boss,' I said, straight out.

'Look, it's quite straightforward,' DC said, folding his arms and leaning back against the breakfast bar. 'Let's take your situation. We don't pay for your food here at No 10, do we? That wouldn't be fair on the taxpayer. As you know, we've inherited an awful bloody mess from the last lot and . . .'

'I don't do politics, DC,' I said, turning tail.

'Yes, OK, sorry – but listen: we don't pay for your food, do we? Everyone around the place chips in because, you know, you're a popular cat, and everyone wants to ...'

'See me right?'

'Quite. Yes, exactly, they want to "see you right" as you put it.'

'I'm not a charity case, Dave. I earn my keep – what with the mice.'

'And the birds,' DC said, with a raised eyebrow. (I managed to get my chops around a sparrow the other day.)

'But yes, you aren't what I believe is commonly referred to as "a sponger". You help us and we help you – we all help each other, in fact. And that, Larry, is what the Big Society's all about. Simples!'

'OK, OK, I get it – help thy neighbour and all that. But listen, DC, it's not snappy,' I told him. 'You used to be good at all that catchphrase stuff, the slogans and what have you – "Hug a Hoodie" and the rest. No, what you need here, DC, is an acronym.'

'An acronym?' he said, narrowing his eyes, and resting his elbows on the expensive black granite work surface.

'Yes. Let's keep this "simples", as I believe you commonly refer to it – no more "Big Society". Just "BS".'

"BS? BS ... Yes, I rather like it!' He smiled, fixing his gaze on the framed Maggie Thatcher portrait over the sink. 'BS libraries, BS rubbish collections; we should really have a BS minister, come to think of it.'

'Why only one, boss?'

'Yes, yes, you're right! Secretary of State for BS,

Minister of State for BS, Under-Secretary of State for BS. I'll get Boy George on to it.'

DC put his Wills and Kate mug down and looked me in the eye. 'You know, Larry, I'm really glad we had this chat.' And off he went.

'Don't forget the BS Tsar,' I shouted after him, 'and the BS task force!'

I do like DC, but sometimes he can be a bit of a muppet.

Sunday 20 February

A BBC journalist arrived today to interview the PM. It wasn't the bald bloke with the specs who's always out front, microphone in hand, but he did look familiar. I think he has his own show on a Sunday morning, only nobody watches it because *Hollyoaks* is on the other side at the same time. They set up a cosy chat in the white room, where plenty of natural light floods in through tall sash windows and a commanding fireplace sits on one side of the room.

DC was as smooth and well-mannered as an eligible bachelor at a debutante ball, as ever. Well, it's the way these toffs are brought up, isn't it? Gabby*,

---

* Sam Cam calls Gabby 'a bag carrier' but I don't know why. After all, a bird without a bag is like a cat without a collar – not a sight you often see.

the girl who always stands and watches him deliver his patter, arms folded like a nervous mum, said afterwards it was a blinding performance (or words to that effect).

But there's only so much chatter about VAT and fuel duty a cat can absorb, and a few minutes into DC's interview I started to drop off. How was I to know that the rat pack were sneaking about making a nuisance of themselves, messing with the TV cables and clambering over the sound equipment?

I only woke up again when I heard my name and realized the BBC bloke was asking Dave all about me. DC said I was settling in fine and he was confident I'd be catching rats before long. I felt myself swelling with pride and rose from my spot under the window where I'd been snoozing, arching my back, stretching and purring loudly. (OK, I hold my paws up: I was preening for the cameras.) But at that very moment, they stopped rolling, sending the crew into a right old panic. 'Power cut,' I thought. 'Would you Adam and Eve it?'

It was then that I clocked them: four rats in the corner, two of them staring right at me and pointing; one of them bent double with laughter and another with his trap around the camera lead. He'd only gone and gnawed straight through it as if it were a cheese sandwich! The nerve!

Before I could move, they'd scarpered, bolting through a makeshift hole in the skirting boards and back to their hiding place deep in the bowels of No 10. I don't think the BBC bloke was any the wiser but I could feel DC glaring at me. If cats could blush I would have turned crimson. As it was, I just slunk off back to the events room as quietly as I could, my tail clamped firmly between my legs.

Monday 21 February

They say cats always land on their feet, but I've been in enough scrapes to know that isn't always the case. I ended up on my back only this morning after I came nose to nose with Nick Clegg, DC's young assistant. Talk about a bruising encounter. I was minding my own business, sat on the arm of a chair in the ground-floor office where DC works – they call it 'the Den' because it's so small and cosy – when Nicky strode in and plonked himself down, pushing me straight off, and ignoring my loud squeal as I hit the floor.

I was none too pleased, but when I had a word in DC's shell-like this evening he told me to cut Nicky some slack.

'His approval ratings are at an all-time low,' the boss whispered to me, although judging by the glint in his eye, he didn't look too sorry about it. I dare say they'd be lower still if the great British public could see the way he knocked me off my perch today.

What have the Lib Dems got against cats? One of their councillors in Birmingham fessed up to murdering some poor moggy a few days ago after he took a swipe at his grandson. He went totally Radio Rental and battered the little fella to death with a walking stick.

Not so long ago, the wife of a Lib Dem MP found out he had a fancy woman and apparently sneaked into her house and catnapped her kitten! I blame the geezer, who has admitted to being a 'love rat'. Where there's trouble, there's always a rodent.

And there's me thinking all Lib Dems were like that TV comedian Lembit Opik off *I'm a Celebrity* – a bit odd but ultimately harmless. Turns out they're more like a few of the felines I've encountered over the years – fluffy on the outside, but hard as nails underneath. Best thing for it is to give the lot of 'em a wide berth, I reckon.

Tuesday 22 February – morning

I've been under DC's roof for exactly a week and I still haven't got close to one of those beady-eyed blighters. The nearest I've come to getting my mush around a rodent is when I pounced on that sparrow in the Downing Street rose garden. I was quite pleased with myself – only the boss didn't look too impressed when I dropped it at his feet.

'The foxes can take care of the birds, old chap,' DC said. 'You just concentrate on the rats, eh?'

I was tempted to tell him to stick his job and find someone else to come and do his dirty work for him, but I won't survive on the outside if I get a reputation as a quitter.

The problem is, I'm a bit like a London cabbie who hasn't finished doing 'the knowledge', which means I'm operating with one paw tied behind my back. These rats have had the run of the place for months, after all, and Downing Street is far bigger than you'd imagine when you look at the gaff from out front.

Behind that famous black door, No 10 is enormous. There are more than 100 rooms in this place – and I know because I've only just finished counting. Just when you think you've discovered everything there is to see you realize there's a whole new building to explore.

No 10 is actually three big old Georgian places knocked together, spread over four floors, with no shortage of nooks and crannies for those rats to exploit – and a small flat sits above the PM's offices where Georgie Boy lives during the week.

DC and the family have made their home in the larger apartment next door at the top of No 11, just like Blair did when Gordon Brown was Chancellor, because they need the extra space. The third place, No 12, is at one end of Downing Street, and yet another building, the Cabinet Office – where Nicky Clegg works – can be reached through a long corridor at the back of No 10.

It's all very confusing. Don't get me wrong, I know central London streets like the back of my paw, but finding your way around this place is a different kettle of fish. It's hardly surprising those rats are always one step ahead of me.

When I'm asleep on my Wills and Kate cushion I can hear them scrabbling around under the floor-boards, and they have a labyrinth of drains and sewers to make use of as well. In fact, I'm sure that's where they spend most of their time, emerging every now and then to give me the run-around and embarrass me in front of the world's media.

Tuesday 22 February – afternoon

I decided to have a poke around again this afternoon, once Harriet had fed me, to see if I could find a map or a floor plan – even the deeds to this place, or the architects' plans, would make it easier to sniff out those rodents.

I looked behind a door on the first floor, but it was full of crockery and not much else, and I checked the basement I explored briefly on my first day without much joy. So eventually I took a deep breath and saun-tered, without knocking, into DC's office next to the room with the big oval table I like to stroll across every now and again when no one's around.

Eventually, I found a metal filing cabinet marked 'personnel' behind his deserted desk. Inside, there were files on everyone – even George Osborne. It turns out George's real name is Gideon, which makes me wonder what he's all about. Who changes their name, after all? And if you were going to change it, why choose 'George'? 'I'm surprised the little upstart didn't opt for Marmaduke,' Mrs C said, when I asked her about it later. A folder with a passport-sized photo of my boat race fastened to the front with a paperclip contained all manner of personal information about Yours Truly. It listed my weight (9lb, since you ask), height and pedigree ('undetermined'). A box headed 'aliases' had been left blank by the No 10 pen-pusher who'd filled it in, but there were detailed notes about my 'personality defects', my weaknesses and something called my 'motivation'.

If Wikileaks ever got hold of this stuff, it could go global, I thought.

I noticed the file had been signed off by someone called 'Hilton', but none of it really made much sense to me.

According to my file, the staff down at Battersea had told No 10 I had a 'strong predatory drive'. 'Before coming to Battersea he was a stray, so he is used to fending for himself on the streets,' they'd said. A final page at the back was marked 'Classified'.

'Nothing is ever guaranteed,' this Hilton bloke had written. 'But his behaviour in Battersea has convinced us that he is up to the job.'

As you can see, expectations are sky high. So where are the little buggers hiding? At least now I can finally roam around the place undisturbed. For the first few days, I couldn't go anywhere without being petted. Secretaries and senior civil servants would drop to their knees the moment they saw me; I don't know how the likes of Cheryl Cole cope with all that adulation.

Wednesday 23 February – morning

I knew I'd overslept this morning when I opened my eyes and clocked Phillip and Holly on the portable telly that sits in the corner of the events room. *This Morning* doesn't start till 10.30 and they were already wrapping up the show. I wonder how long it'll be before DC is on that couch? Tony Blair was sat there so often my old mum, God rest her soul, used to think he was one of the presenters. She always said Tony was her favourite, although she did have a habit of getting him mixed up with Dr Hilary off *GMTV* towards the end. She didn't know if she was coming or going in her last few months – a bit like Blair himself really.

I gave myself a bit of a clean and wandered through to the press room, where the papers are spread out of a morning.

A few of DC's baby-faced advisors were stood around a desk reading a copy of the *Daily Mail* with concerned looks on their faces.

'Oh rats,' I thought. 'Don't tell me those rodents have been doing sprint relays down Downing Street again.'

As I wandered in, one of the girls nudged the young bloke in a smart suit and loafers standing next to her and they all left the room, heads down, in embarrassed silence. Talk about getting the cold shoulder.

I had a butcher's at the papers myself, scanning the front pages just like DC does when he shuffles in first thing before his 8 a.m. meeting. There was no mention of our furry friends, but the *Mail* was still open on the page DC's teenage helpers had been gawping at. The story said some random geezer is claiming I belong to his aunt in Bermondsey. He's even set up a Facebook site demanding I'm returned 'home'.*

What a load of cobblers! I did have an uncle who once lived on the Isle of Dogs, as it happens, but I never liked the sound of the place as a kitten and I always refused to visit. I felt a proper Charlie when

---

* It turned out the guy was having everyone on, which just goes to show those papers will publish any old rubbish. To be honest, it makes me wonder why the bloody hell everyone in this place is so obsessed with them.

I found out very few canines actually live there, but even then I hardly ever ventured east. It's too much of a stretch from the manor where I was raised in the shadow of Battersea Power Station and Albert Bridge.

Anyway, this fella in the *Daily Mail* reckons my real name is 'Joe'. The truth is I'll answer to whatever name I'm given after a little while (within reason) but I told DC today I'm going nowhere – least of all Millwall. They're not too civil to Chelsea fans like me around there.

Wednesday 23 February – afternoon

All the talk at No 10 is about a bloke called Muammar Gaddafi. It goes without saying that anyone with the nickname 'Mad Dog' is never going to be my cup of tea, but this guy sounds particularly unsavoury. And he wears sunglasses all the time, which is always a bit sus, if you ask me.

It's all kicked off in the Middle East and this Gaddafi geezer is trying to cling on to power in Libya, but it looks like the writing's on the wall for him, especially now DC has got involved.

All this stuff is well above my pay-grade, but I've heard the boss on the blower to President Obama and the other little Nicky – Sarkozy – and they're chewing over whether or not to send in the Apaches. Now, I'm no armchair general, but I'd say that means curtains for old Mad Dog, sooner or later.

DC has become quite the diplomat of late. He jetted off to Cairo yesterday, where another despot called Mubarak has been given his marching orders (that's what these people are called once we've fallen out with them or stopped selling them arms: 'despots' or 'tyrants').

It's a pity, because I quite like the sound of the Egyptians. Apparently they used to hold us cats in high regard back in the day. They even had a cat goddess called Bastet. Sensible lot those pharaohs.

When DC's away, Nicky boy usually takes charge, only he jetted off on a school skiing trip yesterday, leaving Willy Hague to mind the shop.

Hague is a follically challenged fella with a black belt in karate who's forever jetting around the world to places the scribblers call 'trouble spots'. The hacks used to refer to him as 'the Mekon' on account of his oversized bonce. But if you ask me he's more like Superman with a Yorkshire accent; I imagine he wears his M&S underpants outside his trousers when he's at home with his glamorous Welsh missus Ffion. I ask you, what sort of name is that?

Except SuperHague isn't handling the Libya situation too well. A British Airways plane he sent out to Tripoli to rescue 500 stranded Brits came back empty last night and he's getting a roasting in the papers. One of Dave's teenage helpers told me this evening that everything would be fine if only Hague could find something called his 'mojo'. As luck would have it, I spotted the Foreign Secretary heading towards the Downing Street exit this evening, head down, papers in hand, after a tête-à-tête* with one of DC's top civil servants, so I thought I'd offer to help him look for it. Hague just shot me a filthy look and carried on walking. Charming.

Thursday 24 February

One of DC's people must have mislaid the office rota. It turns out Nick Clegg was supposed to be in charge all along, only no one – least of all Nicky himself – remembered! He was even asked by a journalist before he left earlier this week if he was supposed to be minding the shop. 'Yeah, I suppose I am,' Nick said. 'I forgot about that.' Now, I'm no Alastair Campbell, but that doesn't sound like the sort of thing you should let slip to a scribbler. Sure enough, it caused him a fair bit of bother in the press today. Poor Nicky; he can't put a foot right. I hope he was steadier on his feet when he was a ski instructor.

Everyone was relieved when the boss returned late

---

* A tête-à-tête is French for 'head to head', by the way. I'm learning far more by hanging around this gaff than I ever did at school.

last night to take charge, sweeping into No 10 in his new Jag. He's already had a late-night chat on the blower with Barack and there are rumours the SAS might be in Libya as we speak, hatching an evacuation plan. It's all very exciting, or it might be if Jeremy Hunt, the Culture Secretary, hadn't gone on the radio this afternoon and let it slip that the boys in black were about to go into action.

Boy George said that Scottish Radio 4 presenter wasn't too wide of the mark just before Christmas when he stuck a 'c' in front of Hunt's last name and had to apologize for turning the air blue. In fact, he only ever refers to him these days as the 'hulture secretary'. I told him all that was before my time, but I knew exactly what he was getting at.

DC is just back from a short visit to Pakistan, only he caused a bit of a stir on the flight home. A young guy from the *Sunday Mirror* had written something he didn't like, so DC came right out and called him an unspeakable word — within earshot of the rest of the scribblers an' all. It's not what you expect to hear from an old Etonian, is it? He might call himself the 'heir to Blair' but DC's more like the 'heir to Brown' when it comes to effin' and blinding. Good thing I'm used to 'authentic language'. If you've spent any time at Stamford Bridge, you'll have probably heard worse — just delivered in a rougher accent.

Friday 25 February

DC gets up at 5.30 a.m. every morning to jump in the shower so he can get a few hours' work done before breakfast with the kids. I'm the only one around at that time to keep him company so I often sit on the edge of the bath while he shaves in the big mirror above the bathroom sink and chat to him about the day ahead.

I'm allowed in the Camerons' flat above No 11 a lot more often now, mainly because the children have taken a bit of a shine to me. They like to chase me around the cornflower-coloured sofa in the living room until I get tired and curl up on the window sill that sits above the big white marble kitchen table where DC does his paperwork.

The only run-in I've had with the little 'uns is when I found them playing a board game called 'Mousetrap' one evening before bath-time. I thought they were having a bit of a pop at me on the sly, but when I stopped and thought about it I realized they were probably trying to help. It was quite sweet really.

The Camerons' new home is a beautiful four-bedroom place over two floors, although Mrs C had a few issues with the décor. Apparently she oversaw a huge amount of building work last year to get it shipshape before the family moved from Notting Hill. The tiny kitchen was all Formica surfaces and wooden cupboards, so she had that ripped out for a start. It must have cost the boss a few quid. DC's teenage helpers still complain about all the banging and sawing that went on last summer. It must have given those rats a bit of a headache.

The rest of the flat has had a complete facelift. It's now an apartment any yuppie would be proud of, and the bathroom is particularly special. There are more mirrors in there than at the Versailles Palace. Sometimes the boss talks to himself while he's shaving, like a boxer preparing for a big fight, tightening his tie, fixing his cufflinks and repeating the same few phrases as he stares at his reflection. Only he has an odd way of psyching himself up.

'You're not posh,' he says. 'You use the NHS. You send your kids to state school. You support Aston Villa.' I suppose he's trying to come across like an average Joe. I think that's why he likes to spend time with me – someone who knows his *Coronation Street* from his *EastEnders*.

'Hair combed to the right or to the left?' DC asked this morning, playing with his parting.

'To the right, guv,' I said. 'I would've thought that was obvious.'

'What about the tie?' he asked me. 'Are spots a bit too old-fashioned? What would the man on the street say?'

'He'd probably say: "Nice tie, Dave, but is there any chance you could spend less time preening in the mirror and more time dealing with the deficit?"'

DC shot me an anxious look.

'And take those flag of St George cufflinks off,' I said. 'They're a bit EDL, if you know what I mean.'

'I thought it might appeal to white-van man,' DC replied.

I had to stifle a snigger. The boss hasn't met a van driver since that tattooed bloke from Heal's delivered the SMEG fridge for Samantha's new kitchen.

Saturday 26 February

So, as I've already said, the geezer in charge of the money is called George Osborne, but everyone calls him 'Boy George' on account of the fact he looks so fresh-faced.

DC and Boy George are a double act, a bit like Ant and Dec, but George is the junior partner, for the time being, at least, working out of No 11 while the boss runs the show next door. George sounds almost as squeaky as one of the rats when he opens his trap, but some people around here reckon he's been having sessions with a speech therapist to try and lower his voice, just like Mrs Thatcher did all those years ago. DC says he's trying to acquire 'gravitas' but I haven't got a Danny La Rue what he's on about. Personally I reckon he's after the top job eventually and he's trying to sound the part.

It may be the weekend but George and DC never

stop. They were stuck in the PM's office for hours this afternoon going through the budget, the big speech Boy George has to make next month about how he's going to balance the books.

'Can we really get away with making all these cuts now?' DC said.

'We haven't got a choice, Prime Minister,' George replied. 'The last lot left an awful mess behind and ...'

'I know that, George, but it's a bit of a gamble. We don't want the recovery to stall before it's even started, and people do seem to be getting rather irate about all these services that are being shut down. There was a demo outside my local library last week.'

'Now don't go all wobbly on me, Dave,' George said. 'We just blame local councils for all that. And besides, fortune favours the brave!'

DC looked a little unsure but Boy George can play him like a ukulele.

'By the way, I thought you were splendid at PMQs today,' he told him.

Seems I'm not the only one who knows how to climb the greasy pole around here.

Sunday 27 February

I like to get up at the same time as DC because Downing Street is at its quietest and I can patter around the place undisturbed. Only the cleaners are here at this time of the morning, clocking in long before Hilton and the 200 or so people who work at this gaff arrive.

It's a godsend, to be truthful, because even now I'm struggling to get my bearings and I wouldn't want anyone to catch me roaming around the place looking lost. It's impossible to keep a secret in this place and word might get back to DC that I don't have a good sense of direction. I'm still trying to impress my new employers, after all.

Even the entrance hall is bigger than you might expect. Its chequered floor of black-and-white tiles is shiny and slippery. When I run across it I slide all over the shop like one of those C-list soap stars on *Dancing on Ice*. I bet those rats negotiate it far more nimbly than I can.

Beyond the hallway is the sweeping staircase, which leads up to the first and second floors, with portraits of past prime ministers on the wall. You've probably seen it on TV. They are paintings from Sir Robert Peel to the pre-war PMs and photographs after that, with an understated black-and-white shot of Tony Blair towards the end.

'Very New Labour,' DC once muttered.

There's no picture of Gordon Brown because his office haven't provided one yet, according to Harriet; she says he was never the best-organized of bosses.

I was basking in the early morning sunlight pouring through the kitchen window this morning when DC and Sam traipsed through – Dave in his towelling dressing gown, Sam in her velour tracksuit – and took up their usual positions at the breakfast table.

Sam told DC he should do something a bit different when the time comes for his own picture to go up on that wall, 'although obviously,' she added quickly, 'that's some way off.'

'Would you sit for Banksy?' she said, peering at him mischievously over the top of her copy of *The Lady*.

DC nearly choked on his muesli.

'I assume you're joking,' he said, placing his spoon on the table and bending down to tie the shoelaces of his fluorescent running shoes.

'And by the way, do you have to buy that rag?'

'It's rather good actually,' Sam said defiantly.

'I'm sure it is, darling, but isn't it edited by that awful Johnson woman – Boris's sister?'

('BoJo' and his family are none too popular around here, although I can't quite fathom why.)

'I've no idea,' Sam replied. She's fibbing, of course. I know for a fact she only subscribes to wind DC up.

I smiled to myself, yawned ostentatiously and stretched out on the window sill.

Monday 28 February – morning

I sprinted down the spiral staircase first thing this morning and made my way to the entrance hall. My plan was to map the place out in my head, starting at the front and working backwards, but I decided to have a bit of a doze first, just to collect my thoughts, you understand, and curled up on the same wooden chair I'd used when Prince Charles came calling.

Some distinguished posteriors have polished that wooden seat over the years. It's known as the Churchill chair, because the great old man used to sit on it during the war, although since President Obama visited a few years back and told staff how he'd once used it himself, some people now call it the Obama chair.

Now I don't want to come across as the big 'I am', but I've renamed it the 'Larry chair' on account of the fact it's already one of my favourite places in Downing Street – along with the photocopier in the events room and Mrs C's knickers drawer.

Monday 28 February – afternoon

I had my first proper sighting of one of the little buggers today, up close and personal like. I was curled up in my basket, minding my own business and wondering what I'd wear to the royal wedding, when I sensed him, a looming presence in the corner of the events room. He was crouching by the skirting board as bold as brass, daring me to go after him.

I could see his beady eyes giving me the once over,

sussing me out. Now I know how DC feels when he faces Miliband across the despatch box in the old H of C. He's a big fella too, this rat, but quick on his feet – before I could move a whisker he'd done one, squeezing through a tiny hole between the wall and the floorboards. I can't quite put my paw on it, but there's something about this rodent that makes me think he's running the show. I reckon he's the brains of the outfit, the ace in the pack, the criminal mastermind. He's King Rat: the one rodent I simply have to get my paws on.

MARCH 2011

Tuesday 1 March – morning

I told DC this morning that I'd come face to face with the rat, but I swear that bloke doesn't always listen.

'Pass me the shaving foam,' he said absent-mindedly, his arm extended.

'Hold your horses,' I replied. 'I'm not your bleeding valet.' I think he sometimes forgets he's not at Eton anymore.

The boss can be a decent bloke one on one, to be fair, and we had a bit of a heart-to-heart about the rat situation.

'I've got rats to contend with too, Larry,' DC said. 'They're called MPs. The Labour ones are particularly ghastly, I have to say.'

He told me all about how the opposition lot hang around in the Strangers bar at the Commons, a small room on the ground floor which leads on to a terrace overlooking the Thames, drinking pints of bitter.

'Total oiks, some of them,' he said.

'I know the type,' I told him. 'Fat northern blokes who look like they should be doing stand-up in working men's clubs?'

'Precisely, although they can handle their drink. I'd be drinking if I were them, quite frankly. But I just wish our boys wouldn't try to match them, pint for pint, even if it can have hilarious consequences on occasion.'

'Do tell,' I said.

'Well, one evening, I think it was the Finance Bill vote. Readings were going on into the early hours. One of the new MPs got so sloshed that he opted out in the end, saying he was in a state that was "inappropriate for voting." Someone said he'd dozed off.'

'Come off it! What was he called?'

'That's the best bit,' DC said, leaning towards me. 'His name was Reckless!'

'Should've been Legless.'

DC said another MP, a Labour man, ended up having a punch-up with a newspaper vendor in another bar next door, and he told me how the *Mail on Sunday* have a snapper stationed over on the other side of the river from the Commons at St Thomas' Hospital, with a long lens trailed permanently on the terrace.

'It's a pity I can't pop down there and pick up the odd bit of intelligence for you,' I told DC.

The boss just smiled.

And then he told me all about the 'awkward squad' and their ringleader David Davis, who's known as 'Double D' to his followers. He was raised on a rough estate and he's come up the hard way, not like DC. His old man used to work at Battersea Power Station, right next door to the cats' and dogs' home where I served time, so the two of us would probably have a lot to talk about.

The problem is that Double D is always stirring up trouble for the boss on that terrace with the river view and a lot of the boss's backbenchers are all ears at the moment. Half of them were expecting jobs in the new government, only after the coalition deal was struck they lost out to a load of Lib Dems no one's ever heard of. No wonder a fair few of them are in a rebellious mood.

He sounds like a tough old so and so, this Double D character – apparently he used to be in the SAS, and people say he still flies planes occasionally and goes on the odd parachute jump.

'Just remember, Larry, you're not the only one with vermin to worry about,' DC said. And then he slunk off to his desk.

If I didn't know better I'd say the boss is scared that Double D might duff him up behind the bins or something.

Tuesday 1 March – afternoon

I'm not the new cat on the block anymore. DC's hired some new geezer to advise him on how to handle the scribblers and snappers. He started work this week.

Craig Oliver turned up at the Downing Street gates carrying an iPad, with a 'man bag' slung over his shoulder and a cycling helmet in his left hand. Fair play to the bloke, I thought, at least he'd done his homework – it seems like everyone at this place prefers two wheels to four.

They should really get Harriet to stick one of those signs up: 'You don't have to be a cyclist to work here, but it helps.'

This Olly character had a pair of headphones draped around his neck – huge cans that look like they cost a few quid. The barnet's thinning a bit and there's the slightest hint of a paunch, but like a lot of people around here, I reckon he's trying to cling on to his youth.

I overheard him telling Boy George this afternoon those headphones were designed by Dr Dre. I had a giggle to myself when I heard that one; George is so stiff he probably thinks Dr Dre is the government's Chief Medical Advisor.

Mrs C, on the other hand, has got the 'Best of NWA' on her iPod playlist. I know because 'F*** tha Police' was blaring out in the flat upstairs when DC had the head of the Met around the other day. The boss had to borrow his truncheon and bang on the study ceiling until Sam Cam turned the volume down.

I'm a bit worried Olly won't fit in. I realized when he opened his gob that he's a Scotsman, and apparently he went to a normal school like the rest of us. Even worse, he was an executive at the BBC before he took this gig, which is almost as bad as chairing the Toxteth branch of the Socialist Workers' Party in DC's eyes.

But if Olly could keep the media off my back it would be helpful. One of the papers said yesterday they'd been told by a 'senior Downing Street source' I'd shown absolutely no interest in rats or mice. In fact, this snout let slip I was displaying a 'distinct lack of killer instinct'. I thought that was bang out of order, especially since I've barely even been allowed outside yet, but I'm starting to realize this place is leakier than one of Jeffrey Archer's fur-lined waterbeds.

I overheard Mrs C this morning complaining the kids have got fleas. 'I knew we shouldn't have sent them to state school,' she said.

Wednesday 2 March

There are no doors and very few walls separating No 10 and No 11, which makes the place seem even bigger. But, like a cracked old cup that's been badly repaired using superglue, you can still see the join between the two pieces.

If you do a left when you enter through the front door, and walk down a long corridor, you'll notice the pattern of the carpet changes suddenly halfway down.

It wasn't planned that way.

Shortly after the Blairs arrived in '97, Tony's missus decided the carpets needed replacing throughout both buildings, only the bloke next door, Gordon Brown, got jumpy about the price of the project (well, I suppose he did have a reputation for prudence in them days). 'How much will it cost?' he asked. He clearly didn't like the answer, because when the carpet-fitters came, they were told to rip up the No 10 flooring but stay well clear of No 11, and by the time Brown did replace the carpet on his side of the fence, when it was simply too threadbare to put off any longer, they'd stopped selling the pattern Cherie had ordered in for No 10 and he had to settle for a different design. It just goes to show that all that talk about 'joined-up government' was a load of baloney. Tony and Gordon were barely on speaking terms, after all, so they barely even knew what the other was up to half the time. At least Boy George and DC are forever nattering away.

Thursday 3 March

These budget cuts DC is always banging on about must be starting to bite – Harriet bought some Lidl cat food in today. It was surprisingly good if I'm honest, although I'm not too keen on the commemorative dishes they're serving it up in. It's a bit off-putting wolfing down a no-frills supper with a picture of Prince William's physog staring back at you.

The boss sits at the kitchen table each morning from

quarter to six, spending a few hours going through the paperwork his civil servants pack into his red boxes the previous evening, before having his breakfast with Mrs C and the children. It sounds soft, I know, but I missed being part of a family when I was roaming the streets and then locked up in the slammer, although the people at Battersea were very nice.

When Mrs C reached down and took my bowl away this morning (before I'd even finished licking it clean, mind), lifting it high above my head, I could read the words 'made in China' stamped on the bottom. Sign of the times, innit?

Don't get me wrong, I've got nothing against the Chinese – alright, so there were some horrible scare stories doing the rounds at Battersea concerning the takeaways down SW11 way. But it was the dogs that started that rumour and we all know they're a bit sensitive when it comes to exotic eating habits.

After Mrs C had rinsed out my bowl, she got the hoover out, which was my cue to leave.

I think she puts it on deliberately sometimes, just to get rid of me.

Friday 4 March

Nick Clegg had a terrible night on Thursday: he lost his deposit up in Barnsley. I had no idea he was buying a house, to be honest, and God only knows why he'd want one up there, but he's proper upset about this deposit business and no mistake.

He held a crisis meeting with DC this morning and, at one point, from my favourite step at the bottom of the winding staircase, I heard him make a list of demands.

He's going to ask if he can stay out past midnight in a minute, I thought. Or ask if he can have his own set of keys.

It turned out Nick was more concerned about 'the big picture', although quite which picture he was on about I can't really say – there are quite a few of 'em in this place. He said he wanted more out of the Coalition and a greater say over policy – something he can show his supporters, assuming he has any left, to prove to them that getting into bed with DC was worthwhile.

'People used to agree with me, Dave,' he said. 'Now I can't even show my face in my own constituency.'

'Hmm. That business with Forgemasters, the engineering company, probably didn't help,' DC mused. 'Perhaps we should have given them that loan after all. They're a huge employer in Sheffield, you know.'

'Of course I bloody well know,' Nick said. 'It could cost me my seat!'

'Don't worry, Nicky boy, we can always sort you out with another one.'

'I don't want another one. I've got a lovely place up there and ...'

Nick took a deep breath and stood up.

'Look, Dave, you know I believe in grown-up politics,' he said.

'Grown-up politics, yes,' DC said archly.

'Well, in that case perhaps you can explain to me why you never treat me like a grown-up!' He stormed out, slamming the door behind him.

I snuck into the room, squeezing in quietly as usual, and shot DC an anxious look.

'That was spectacular,' I said.

'That boy's nothing but trouble,' he sighed. 'In fact, I think I'm going to have to ground him for being cheeky.'

Saturday 5 March

'Gramps' is here. I think he lodges in the loft. Sam said over breakfast this morning she was going to buy him a coffin to sleep in. I think she was joking but then if Boden did coffins those two would probably order one in.

Gramps pops in whenever he's in town, the miserable old sod, always carrying a thick bundle of newspapers under his arm, and DC always seems keen to roll out the red carpet for him.

He lives in New York now but he visits a lot, usually arriving through the tradesmen's entrance to avoid the scribblers and snappers out the front.

I'm not sure whose grandfather he is, and I'm sure he calls himself 'Murdoch', but then these posh types have all sorts of nicknames for each other, don't they? He's obviously dead tight with DC: The boss is on the phone to Gramps all the time.

'Do you think Barack Obama really likes me or is he just, you know, pretending?' I heard the boss ask the other day.

Gramps usually sits in front of the telly when he stays over, flicking through Sky channels of an evening and muttering to himself, but this time he was in a better mood. Apparently his company had a big deal waved through by the government today.

'Well, that's hardly surprising is it?' I said to DC with a wink when I passed him on the stairs.

'Alright, that's quite enough,' DC snapped back, his voice slightly strained. 'If you'd been following the news you'd know we consulted all the relevant independent regulatory bodies before we approved that takeover, and we followed their legally binding advice to the letter.'

I honestly thought he was going to give me a kick.

'Calm down, mate,' I said as I slunk past him. 'I'm not a *Guardian* journalist.'

'Bloody cat,' I heard him mutter as he walked into the Den, and then, to no one in particular: 'Who put the BBC News Channel on? I told them we only watch Sky News when Rupert's here.'

'Or Fox,' I said, louder than I should have done.

It was only then I spotted one of those flaming rats sat beside an armchair, casual as you like, standing on the remote control with a big grin on his face.

I didn't feel half as cocky after that.

Sunday 6 March

Downing Street was even quieter first thing this morning. All the top Tories were at their spring conference in Cardiff and DC was giving a speech. Thankfully they didn't sing the Welsh national anthem, so DC didn't have to try and hum along like that Redwood bloke tried to a few years back. (If memory serves he only knows the words to two songs: 'Girlfriend in a Coma' and 'I Vow to Thee My Country', plus the first verse of 'God Save the Queen'.)

But then there was a bit of a panic about Prince Andrew. One of his rich American acquaintances is being investigated by Swiss police for some (allegedly) unspeakable misdemeanours and the papers are getting excited.

DC was travelling back from Cardiff, but when Gabby put the boss on speakerphone he said he had some sympathy for Andy. He reckons you can't vet every person you meet on the off chance they get up to no good in private, which might explain why he was always so civil to that Bunga Bunga fella before it emerged that he was busy romancing his way around Italy.

The trouble with Randy Andy is he does a government job, flying around the world drumming up business for British firms, but he's put his foot in it far too often lately and the papers seem to think this could be the last of his proverbial nine lives.

It's situations like these that Oliver was hired to deal with and before you could say 'off with his head', he'd been summoned to Downing Street, day of rest or no day of rest.

I was sat in the corner of the Den when the *spinmeister* arrived, looking flustered, shirt hanging out of his trousers and Dr Dre headphones dangling out of his jacket pocket.

DC jumped on him straight off.

'Have we got a line?' he demanded, his voice crackling over the phone.

Boy George took his wallet out of his top pocket and started to look through it.

'I think he means a line for the press,' Olly piped up, clearing his throat decisively.

'Well, Prince Andrew can't carry on mixing with these characters,' he said, shaking his head disapprovingly.

'But on the other hand, he's not actually done anything wrong, apart from embarrass the Queen.'

'I think she's used to it,' DC said down the phone line. Boy George nodded.

'On the one hand, he's entitled to a private life,' Oliver continued, his finger pressed to his bottom lip. 'On the other hand, choosing unsuitable friends does betray a certain . . . lack of judgement.'

'Yes, but what are we going to do?' DC snapped.

Oliver shuffled from one foot to the other. 'Well, on the one hand . . .'

I could picture DC in the back of the car, rolling his eyeballs. Boy George shook his head impatiently.

'We shouldn't back him,' Oliver said. 'But we shouldn't sack him either.'

'Right,' DC said, hesitantly.

'Yes, but . . . no, but . . . yes, but,' George whispered under his breath.

Oliver blushed slightly.

'Don't worry, mate,' I said as I brushed past the bottom of Olly's beige chinos. 'You'll get the hang of it eventually.'

Monday 7 March

Your first week in the new job. I remember it only too well. You keep forgetting where the drinks machine is and have to ask the way to the khazi. Everyone's pretending not to notice you, but they're all nattering about you down the boozer after work. I feel for Oliver. I really do.

I was enjoying an early morning break this morning, gazing out of the window on the first-floor landing, when I noticed the poor bloke standing on the pavement on Whitehall, looking as dishevelled as Boris Johnson on a windy day.

The copper manning the big black steel security gates at the end of Downing Street had just started his first shift of the week and didn't recognize the new boy, so the plod wouldn't let him through the security scanner.

Oliver looked as sick as a Lib Dem MP with a tiny minority when DC's convoy swept straight past, leaving him stranded at the front gate arguing the toss, and sicker still when he clocked the long-lens camera over the road.

He shouted at the car, but no one inside could hear him – all that bulletproof metal and glass means DC's jag is as good as soundproofed.

DC was on his way to a cabinet meeting up in Derby – he likes to spend a few hours outside London once or twice a month – and Oliver should have been on the back seat, briefing him on the day ahead.

Finally, he persuaded the cop to let him in and disappeared inside, and within thirty seconds he was sprinting up the stairs, straight past my comfortable seat next to the window and into his office. A few minutes later, he marched back out again, a phone pressed to each ear, barking 'Westminster Cars' into the first handset and 'Whitehall Taxis' into the second. I watched as he re-emerged on to the street, and flagged down a black cab.

One of DC's teenage helpers, who had crowded around the window by now, shouted: 'Taxi for Oliver!' I doubt it'll be the last time Oliver hears that phrase around here.

Tuesday 8 March

It's taken me nearly three weeks to clock it, but I don't reckon these rats are from around here.

I had a run-in with one of them in the Terracotta Room today (it hasn't been terracotta for long; it used to be green, and before that, blue, but I reckon Nicky Clegg will have it painted a lovely shade of 'Lib Dem yellow' before long).

It's a wonderful place to spend a lazy few hours of an afternoon. I like to stretch out on the old patterned rug that covers the polished wooden floor and gaze up at the gold-leafed ceiling. But not today.

I was just beginning to unwind when I spotted King Rat scarper through the doorway, so I dashed behind one of the wheels of Baby Flo's pram and crouched down, ready to pounce.

King Rat hid behind the wheel of DC's old bike –

the Terracotta Room houses a lot of junk that might be stuck in the garage, if only this place was common enough to have one. Then four of King Rat's mates raced in to join him. My ticker was beating louder than the parliamentary division bell, I don't mind admitting.

They spotted me crouching behind the Flo-mobile, looked me in the eyes, bold as brass, then ran over to the teak chest of drawers where the PM hides his Eton and Oxford memorabilia,* quicker than an MP racing from the Strangers bar to make a late-night vote.

Then they disappeared through a hole under the cupboard so small even the Speaker would have struggled to clamber through it. Only they left a few clues behind.

I managed to retrieve a fold-up map of the M1 that was tucked under the hubcap of DC's bike and I found a rolled-up copy of *Viz* on the floor next to it, alongside a miniature dictionary of cockney dialect. I opened it up and had a gander.

A load of phrases were listed in the right-hand columns. 'You're having a laugh', 'Get a shift on' and the like. And on the left, translations were printed alongside them. I'd opened the book on the 'D' entries and as I read the phrases out loud – 'hadaway', 'howay

---

* I had a peak in there the other day, but all I could find was a wooden tennis racket, an old packet of red Rizla, a Sade CD and a photo of DC and his university mates dressed up in top hat and tails.

man, pet' – it dawned on me. Bloody hell. These rats are Geordies! Is it any wonder they're getting a rise out of making life so difficult for a soft southerner like me?

Wednesday 9 March

They call it the Civil Service, only today it's not too civil and they aren't providing much of a service.

DC described the lot of them as 'enemies of enterprise' in his speech on Sunday afternoon and I reckon they've taken it to heart. I think it was Dave's bezzie mate Steve Hilton who persuaded the boss to have a pop at the smartly turned out paper-shufflers who make sure the country runs smoothly.

Hilton's another of your folically challenged fellas, who roams around the place in a T-shirt and jeans. I haven't met him yet, but I need to get him on side because he and DC are well tight – and it was Hilton's name that was written on the personnel file I found in the boss's filing cabinet. He's obviously a power-broker. I wonder if it was his idea to get me in the first place.

Boy George always refers to Hilton as a 'Svengali' and I don't think the civil servants are too keen on him either because they're always kiboshing his ideas. Consultancy papers get lost behind sofas, policy initiatives are found in recycling bins and lunchtime motivation seminars are cancelled at short notice because people suddenly remember the gym inductions they booked a month ago. No wonder the atmosphere around here is slightly frosty.

Things aren't looking up for me, either. DC was on *The One Show* last night and he didn't give me the wholehearted vote of confidence I was hoping for. (I can't say I've watched it since Adrian and Christine switched to the breakfast sofa on the other side but, then again, who has?)

The interview was as syrupy as the pancakes DC cooked up for the kids yesterday morning, until he was asked about me. The boss said I was settling in well, but he let it slip that I hadn't caught any rats yet. Thanks for sharing that with the nation, Dave. He'll be on the blower to Rentokil if I don't pull my claws out soon. But there's only me on my own pitted against what looks like a load of rough Geordies. Is it any wonder I haven't been throwing myself into the job?

Thursday 10 March

I came across DC at lunchtime stuffing a sandwich down his throat in the No 11 flat. He was relaxing on the bright yellow sofa that sits in the middle of the living room next to Sam's swanky new kitchen.

The PM was flicking idly through a copy of the

Sun. 'MOD pay £22 for a 65p light-bulb,' said the headline on the front page.

'Hmm, I must have a word with Liam Fox about that,' DC said.

Fox is another member of the 'awkward squad', that gang of MPs who are always plotting against DC. They hate the fact the boss has climbed into bed with Nicky's lot and they are looking for an excuse to get rid of him.

DC has given this wily Fox bloke a big job by putting him in charge of the guns and tanks division. I thought the boss had dropped a bit of a clanger by doing that, but Boy George put me right. He said it was a 'master stroke' the other day.

Apparently Fox will have to throw loads of soldiers on the scrapheap and he's already talking about decommissioning the Ark Royal, which won't make him too popular with voters.

'Why do it then?' I asked George.

'That's the beauty of it, old chap,' he said. 'Money's tight, remember? And in any case, I'm the one who sets the defence budget – so Fox doesn't have a choice!'

I'm getting the hand of this politics lark, but I can't waste too much energy on it. After all, I've got an awkward squad of my own to deal with.

DC was still flicking through his copy of the Currant Bun.

'You know, the sports pages in here aren't actually all that bad,' he said. 'I wouldn't object to some more rugby coverage though.'

'I thought you were a football fan?' I said. 'Aston Villa isn't it?'

'Haven't been to Birmingham for years,' DC said. 'Only for party conference and what have you.'

He folded the paper away.

'Can I ask you something, Larry?'

'Anything, DC.'

He started talking about the royal wedding. It turns out only a handful of MPs can go. There's some who will be invited as a matter of course, including all the senior types like Hague and Boy George. (DC calls it 'protocol'. I just call it good manners.)

Others are mates with Charlie, so they might be alright, too, like that big old boy Nicholas Soames – a posh type who's always banging on about how he's related to Winston Churchill. But some, like Spelman, will have to watch it on the box like the rest of us.

'Terrible things, weddings,' DC said 'Like popularity contests, you see.'

I do see. Someone always gets upset if they're not invited to the church, although personally I think it's great when you can rock up to the reception without sitting through the service, like skipping to the dessert without having to touch the starter.

But DC is worried someone on the scent of trouble will end up with their nose out of joint – and he can't afford to make too many enemies in this job.

There will be no shortage of seats reserved at the Abbey for Kate Middleton's family, of course, although even they must be worried some of them won't be guaranteed a place on the pew.

Her uncle George sounds like a bit of a wild boy, for a start, messing with illegal substances and dating lap-dancers. I wouldn't have minded knowing him in my wilder years, I can tell you.

Then there's Kate's mum, Carole, who runs a business with her old man selling party poppers and balloons. I overheard Mrs C calling her a 'trolley dolly' this evening, but I can't figure out why.

I was earwigging from my hideaway in Sam's and Dave's bedroom, a place I found where I can curl up and lie low when the stresses of the job get a bit too much. It's in the top draw of the chest next to Sam's side of the bed, which is crammed full of lingerie made of silk, lace and satin – it's a heavenly bed for a cat.

I could hear Mrs C and the gaffer gossiping about the wedding while they got changed for a Tory party bash being thrown by one of the party's biggest donors, Sir Philip Green – the bloke who owns Topshop. He's a fat-cat if ever I saw one.

'Mail-order confetti and chocolate fountains,' I heard Sam say. 'It's rather tacky isn't it?'

'I shouldn't be too snobby, Samantha,' DC replied. 'How do you think Boy George's lot made their money?'

'Er, wallpaper?' she said.

'Exactly,' he replied. 'And will you please turn down that bloody rap music?'

'It's grime,' she protested. 'Tinie Tempah's new track.'

'Yes, well, whatever it is, it's giving me a headache.'

'You know something, Dave?' Sam sighed. 'You've been no fun since you've been running the country.'

Friday 11 March

DC and the missus had a bit of a lovers' tiff this morning about some bird called Rebekah – all fancy, innit, with a 'K' and not a common old 'double C'. I was relaxing in Sam Cam's knicker drawer, trying to get forty winks, when the ding-dong started and by the time it was over I'd all but given up on getting any shut-eye at all.

'That bloody redhead!' Sam said, while she was furiously drying her hair in the mirror.

'I think she prefers "Titian-haired" actually,' the boss replied.

Mrs C just rolled her eyes. I wonder if she's a little bit jealous of this Rebekah Brooks character?

I did a bit of research on Sam Cam's iPad* this

---

* The girls Sam Cam works with at Smythson presented her with the iPad when she went on maternity leave last year, but she's barely used it since little Flo came along. It's a godsend for me because she always leaves it lying around in its trendy Union Jack case, and it could easily have been designed for paws rather than fingers. God bless that Steve Jobs fella who runs Apple. If he wasn't a Yank I'd tell DC to have a word with the Queen and get him knighted for services to felines.

afternoon and it turns out she's quite a glamorous sort. Imagine Elizabeth the First channelling Vivienne Westwood and you're halfway there. She's striking looking alright, and judging by the fancy clobber she was wearing in the photos I found on Google I reckon she earns a fair few quid too.

It turns out she runs the company that owns the *Sun* and the *News of the World* – and she edited both of those rags at one time or another. Fair enough, DC, I thought; she could make life very difficult for you, my son – very difficult indeed.

From my sanctuary in the top drawer I could hear Sam mentioning that the boss treats Rebekah 'like royalty'.

'She came to Chequers twice last year!' she said. 'Even on your birthday! And why do we always end up at their place when we go back to the constituency?'

'It's not my fault she has a property down the road from us in Oxfordshire,' DC replied. 'And besides, that husband of hers, Charlie, is a jolly good egg. He's an old Etonian you know.'

I can understand Sam being a bit put out about having to pretend she's Rebekah's NBF, as she calls it, but personally I think DC knows which side his bread is buttered. After all, Gramps has something to do with Rebekah's mob and sometimes it feels like he's the one calling the shots around here.

DC told me later that Rebekah's in a spot of bother because a few of those scribblers of hers got up to no good a while back, paying some shady private eye to hack into mobile phones *in search of stories*. So she needs friends in high places and DC needs positive coverage. Boy George told me that's what you call a *'quid pro quo'*, and he should know because he's always meeting up with Rebekah himself.

Still, it's a dangerous game getting involved with hacks. They remind me of those rats, sneaking around the place, scavenging for stories, causing trouble and generally making DC's job a lot trickier than it ought to be.

This evening, long after DC's spat with Sam had been forgotten, the boss had a bit of a laugh with me about what he described as Rebekah's 'regal manner'.

'All those airs and graces,' he said. 'It's a bit rich for a Warrington lass.'

'These northerners can be right scallies, you know,' I teased him. 'I hope you checked all the mantelpieces after she'd visited Chequers?'

'No,' he replied, in a distracted whisper, 'but I did hide one of my old mobile phones behind the copies of *Tatler*. Come to think of it, I haven't seen it since.'

Saturday 12 March

I tell you what, I could get used to travelling in style. I hopped into DC's Jaguar Sentinal this afternoon. He says the colour is 'graphite'. I call it charcoal, but we've agreed to differ. They do like a bit of spin and the posh words, this lot, so who am I to ruin his fun?

The kids were on the back seat with the boss and I didn't fancy getting caught in a heavy-petting session, so I leapt into the boot and lay there undisturbed, grabbing a well-earned bit of shut eye until I heard the soft crunch of wheels on gravel.

DC's chauffeur opened the boot and I felt the gentle warmth of early spring sun on my fur, but I waited until he'd unloaded Sam's weekend bag before I jumped out on to the driveway, stretching my legs and sniffing the fresh country air. We'd pulled up outside a huge old country home, a bit like the one on that ITV show, *Downton Abbey*.

'A des-res in town and a grace-and-favour home in the sticks,' I thought. 'This is the life.'

I've heard Mrs C talk about Chequers before. It's a beautiful old Elizabethan pile, which has been used by PMs for decades, although I shudder to think how many of the local mice must have taken up residence by now. Thankfully, the place is staffed by sailors from the naval base nearby, who keep DC's weekend retreat ticking over like clockwork, and I doubt the rodents are daft enough to show themselves while the place is crawling with military types.

The Camerons had a dinner party tonight. You'd never believe who were the first guests to arrive – only Helena Bonham-Carter and her oddball husband Tim

Burton. What a pair! Those two must be minted, but I've seen stray moggies with better coats.

Bonham-Carter is best mates with Mrs C, who seems to be on friendly terms with a few showbiz types, and she went to the same posh school in London as Cleggy. It looks like the Tories have stolen Nicky's mates as well as his policies.

I counted twenty-four guests around the great table in the main dining room, and there were at least half a dozen children running around Chequers as well.

Entertaining all those high-flying types must be tiring, but Sam is a smart bird, and she primed me earlier in the day about when I should make an entrance.

'Have you met Larry?' she said after coffee had been served, shouting to make herself heard over the sound of the new Mark Ronson album that was playing on her iPad.

That was my cue to wander in and leap on as many laps as I could, doing the old 'meet and greet' bit. But I can't help it – it's the moulting season. And after a vigorous petting from Ms Bonham-Carter, I realised I'd deposited a fair bit of hair all over everyone's glad-rags. Some of the posher types raised objection, especially the ones wearing velvet. So I was politely shown the door shortly after. I didn't mind. I left them to it, drinking brandy and talking about country sports while I explored the cavernous luxury of country living. I could get used to a place like this, I thought. After all, I've got my retirement to think about, although that said I'd better start saving for my pension now. We can't all inherit a fortune, can we, lads?

Sunday 13 March

I hitched a ride back to London last night with one of DC's security detail so I could spend today quietly making plans.

Sundays are always less hectic at No 10 – even the snappers and scribblers out front are fewer in number – and with the Camerons still in the country, there was no need for me to pussyfoot around, trying to steer clear of the kids and minding my 'Ps and Qs'. I even used the Obama chair as a scratching post, just for the hell of it.

I put the rest of the day to good use, mind, laying a few mousetraps that I'd found in the cellar around the Terracotta Room. Alright, it's a fair cop; I know it's cheating, but the emerald-green Smythson notebook I was issued with on my first day as part of my 'golden hello' doesn't make for happy reading and desperate times call for desperate measures.

The only entry on the first page says: 'Rats clocked – 24. Rats whacked – 0.'

I raided Sam's fridge and found some Roquefort

and Dolcelatte, loaded the traps, clambered into the cupboard where DC keeps his Eton memorabilia, sat back and waited.

Then I watched through the gap in the door as a couple of rats shuffled in, casual as you like, and took a good sniff at the cheese from a safe distance – but there was no danger of either of them taking a bite. So I slunk out of the cupboard and back to my basket.

The thing is these rats just don't look hungry, and when you think about it, that's hardly surprising.

Never mind the bin bags out back; there are more than enough places to find food at No 10. There's the small dining room on the second floor, and the state dining room right next to it, with great big kitchens next door where chefs serve the sort of grub that Heston Bloomin' heck fella rustles up at his restaurant.

There's the canteen in the basement, the vending machines in the corridor next door, the finger food served at charity receptions; tea and cucumber sandwiches in the Rose Garden in the afternoon, and coffee and biscuits at every meeting. I haven't even counted the kitchens at No 10 and No 11.

DC has had a portrait of Mrs T taken out of a cosy little first-floor room called the 'Thatcher study' and moved to a bigger office across the way that's rarely used. He says it looks better in a grander setting. I reckon he was spooked because her eyes kept following him around the room.

Monday 14 March

Those rats were making a right racket last night and I couldn't sleep so I made my way down to the Larry chair at around 3 a.m. to see if I could drop off there.

I could feel my eyelids getting heavier after a while, but the sound of two voices put my back up. Ears twitching, I jumped down on to the chequered tiled floor and trotted towards the source of the chatter.

A heavy oak side door had swung open and two middle-aged, pot-bellied blokes were in the tiny room on the other side, standing around drinking cups of tea and gassing about those poor nags that got frazzled at Newbury at the weekend. What a way to go.

They were wearing a uniform of sorts; smart trousers and white shirts with epaulettes, and black shoes polished to a shine so bright I could make out my own reflection in their toecaps.

I stood staring at the image of my own distorted face from a foot or so away, transfixed by the concave cat's face grinning back at me.

Then they clocked me.

'Oh, hello, this here must be Larry,' one of them said to the other.

'He looks like a right little scrapper, doesn't he?' the second one said.

'Yeah, proper little pugilist.'

I didn't know what to make of them at first. After all, I'm not a 'pugilist' – or any other breed, as far as I know – just a street cat with no pedigree and, until a few months ago, no fixed abode.

But these two geezers seemed like salt of the earth types, just like me, with none of the airs and graces DC puts on from time to time. I may have ended up in high office, but I'm proud of my humble roots, all the more so since I started knocking around with all these upper-class types who were born with silver spoons rammed down their cake-holes.

So, after a moment's hesitation I decided to take a closer look. The uniformed men crouched as I approached so they could give me a quick stroke.

'You're here to get rid of these rats, aren't you, mate?' said Harold, the man with salt-and-pepper hair who'd spotted me first.

'Yeah, good luck with that,' added Ted, the smaller one of the two. 'You'll have to find them first though.'*

Harold rose to his feet, putting his mug down on the desk in front of him and turned his back on his friend, who was still busy petting me.

---

* The two blokes didn't have name badges, so I decided to call them Harold and Ted after two of the blokes – one 'red' one 'blue' – who were running the country the last time we had a budget deficit this big.

'Hang about!' he shouted out. 'There's two of the buggers now – right on cue!'

Ted scooped me up in one arm and lifted me towards the desk. I let out a squeal of irritation and struggled to break free, but then I clocked the bank of TV screens right in front of my mush.

I stopped wriggling and hung motionless in mid-air, Ted's hand under my stomach, my arms and legs dangling free, hypnotized by the flickering black and white images before my eyes. My jaw must have hit the floor, even from that great height.

A dozen or more monitors were stacked behind the desk, each of them showing live images of a different Downing Street room. And on the screen furthest to the right you could make out two rodents, staring back at the CCTV camera that was filming their every move.

Below the grainy picture showing their ugly little mugs, their exact location was spelt out in big black letters: 'White Room; first floor, front.'

Rounding up these rats is a tough assignment, but I think I might have stumbled across Mission Control.

Tuesday 15 March

I went wandering today to see if any of those traps I set had snared a rodent or two but it took me a while just to remember where I'd put them.

As if it this place wasn't already confusing enough, I realized today that there's a lift off the corridor that runs from the front door to the Cabinet room at the back of No 10.

I climbed into it this afternoon and after a few minutes the doors closed and it started to move upwards with a jolt. I could feel last night's tuna churning around in my stomach as we ascended, and when the sliding doors opened again, I found myself in Osborne's flat.

Now, I know how those rats can be spotted on one floor one minute and materialize on another seconds later. I thought they were making use of the sewers and the drainpipes that criss-cross this place like a miniature rodent Tube network, but it turns out they've been hitching a ride on the Osborne Express.

There's a second lift at Downing Street an' all, to the west of the entrance hall en route to No 11, so I clambered in that one this morning to see where it would take me.

It opens up into an old-fashioned pantry, just like the one my old nan used to have in her big old house in Putney all those years ago. It was dark but I could make out the silhouettes of a few jam jars and tins of beans, and a sliver of light at the far end of the room suggested a door had been left ajar.

I nudged my way through it, emerging blinking into the brightness, and recognized it immediately as DC's kitchen.

No wonder the boss can leave the flat after I do but

arrive in his office before me. It's pretty special, you have to admit. How many of us can say we catch the lift to work?

You'd think he would have no excuse for ever missing an early morning meeting, but he still turns up late with his hair wet on occasion, looking like he's just stepped out the shower. I suppose it was always the kid who lived closest to the school that turned up late for registration, weren't it?

Anyway, by the time I'd finished travelling in the lift I'd lost a good hour or two, so I rushed around searching for my mousetraps and remembered I'd set one in the corridor next to the canteen behind one of the three vending machines. I approached it with excitement, and a little trepidation – if truth be told I felt a bit queasy – but it was empty apart from a tiny note covered with even smaller scrawled writing that conveyed a simple message. 'Is this the best you can do?' it read. The cheese was gone, of course, and I have no doubt at all it was those rats that scoffed it. For the first time since Harriet helped me get settled in this place I honestly wondered if I might be better off back in Battersea.

Wednesday 16 March

It was nearly 8 a.m. by the time I returned to No 10 this morning after a long night exploring St James's

Park, but it was no lighter than it had been at midnight.

The old house, quiet and lifeless, was as dark as David Miliband's mood on the morning after the Labour leadership contest, but as I crept slowly up the stairs I noticed that pools of light were spilling out from Nick's bedroom and illuminating the heavy, threadbare carpet in the hallway.

I stood up on my back legs and leant on the doorhandle with my front paws until the door swung open. Nicky was wide awake, but he didn't clock me. He was too busy gawping at a 10-inch plasma screen balanced on a heavy oak chair by the side of his bed, watching last night's Oscars.

He must have been rooting for his old mate Colin Firth, who was up for a gong for *The King's Speech*. Firth came out for Nicky's lot when Clegg made a big song and dance about student tuition fees before the election last year, sharing a cuppa down Putney way for the benefit of the snappers. But he dropped them quicker than Tony Blair used to dispose of under-performing cabinet ministers when Nicky struck a deal with DC.

Even so, he was glued to the ceremony, and he broke into a grin as wide as the Thames when Sky News said Firth had won best actor. He didn't even notice when I jumped silently onto his Lib Dem duvet and curled up at the bottom of his bed.

As I drifted off, I realized he must be feeling a bit

like I do. He's star struck, pinching himself that he's met the likes of Firth, and struggling to adjust to the fact he's Dave's little assistant – just like I can't quite get my noodle around my elevated status as DC's chief mouser. It's all happened too fast for me and Nicky. We're both out of our depth.

The phone DC lost at Chequers has turned up. One of the cleaners found it behind the pile of *Tatlers* where the boss hid it when Rebekah Brooks last visited and handed it in to security. It's now safely back at No 10, hidden in a drawer in the side room where Ted and Harold drink tea and stare at CCTV screens night and day.

Phew! I was worried for a while that it might have found its way into a hack's pocket at the *News of the World*.

Thursday 17 March

We had the press in the Pillared Room this evening for a reception.

A few of the hacks have been none too kind about me so I spent some time slaloming between legs in the hope I might trip one of them up. It must be strange to have a single pair of pegs to balance on; I'm surprised you lot don't topple over more often.

In the event, everyone stayed on their feet, but I managed to make a mess of a few trouser legs – rub me up the wrong way, mate, and I'll rub up the wrong way against you.

DC was what Mrs C would call 'clubbable', charming the most hostile scribblers – apart from one bloke from the *Daily Mirror*. They've got this guy from the north-east called Kevin Maguire working for them and he stood in the corner all evening, sipping from a champagne flute and calling the boss 'druggie Dave' behind his back. It's nice to know I'm not the only one who's getting a tough time from Geordies.

Sam did well tonight too, although I couldn't help noticing she screwed her nose up when she took her first sip of white wine. I don't think the plonk they serve up at these dos is up to much. They must have decided to keep the expensive stuff locked away in the government wine cellars, but it's probably just as well – it would have been wasted on this lot.

After the press pack had been ushered out, DC joined Mrs C in the top-floor flat, flopping down on the sofa, and loosening his tie. He glanced over at me, lying on the bright-yellow sofa.

'Shouldn't you be catching rats?' he said.

Then the boss sprang to his feet.

For one horrible moment I thought he'd seen a rat, but luckily for me they haven't set foot in the flat yet.

'Right then,' DC said, rubbing his hands together.

'Now that lot have gone let's pop open a bottle of the decent stuff.'

I just carried on cleaning my face with my paw and pretended to ignore him.

'Splendid!' Sam smiled, up-ending her glass and depositing its contents into a plant pot in the corner of the room.

'Denis Thatcher used to do that, you know,' DC said, smiling.

'Do what?'

'It's not important. Now what are we fancying; Chablis? Pouilly-Fumé?'

'Got any Red Bull?' Sam said.

Friday 18 March

This Hilton bloke is a cycling fanatic, just like DC used to be before he got his prime-ministerial car. He walks in most mornings with his bike saddle and his helmet under his arm.

Hilton has what DC once called 'a relaxed approach to sartorial conventions'. In other words, he's a right old scruff, always wandering around in jeans and T-shirts. Sometimes he doesn't even bother with shoes.

The word is Hilton only wears suits at weddings, funerals and Tory party conferences, and I swear I once overheard him saying he'd sooner be at the second than the last, but DC won't have a bad word said about him. He's even installed Hilton in one of the two large offices near the room with the big table in it where the Cabinet meet twice a week.

Hilton turned up to a posh do this evening in jeans, a white T-shirt and socks. All the guests were high-flying business types wearing expensive whistles. Well you wouldn't arrive to meet the PM in jogging bottoms and a pair of trainers, would you?

Some of them looked a bit taken aback at Hilton's get-up but they were lapping up everything he told them.

I know because I was snaking through the room, brushing against trouser legs and stockinged ankles, in the hope one of the salmon and sour cream blinis they were serving up would end up on the carpet so I could snaffle it. No such luck.

Hilton was banging on about this Big Society idea all evening. In fact, I think it was him who dreamt the whole thing up. Then again I'm told he used to work in advertising, so I suppose talking BS comes naturally.

After the suits had vacated the building I had a butcher's at the traps I'd snuck into the room before the party began (as I've mentioned already, blood, guts and gore aren't really my style). I know the rodents can't resist a get-together, what with all the food wastage that inevitably slips from hands and out of the corners of mouths and on to the floor beneath – a morsel enough to feed a family – so I'd used the opportunity to stick at least half a dozen of those tiny cardboard cages around the perimeters of the ostentatiously decorated room. I checked them more in hope than expectation – and perhaps even with a hint of desperation if I'm honest – but they were as empty as the last one was.

But there was a message, of sorts, tucked away inside the very last one I got to. A piece of A4 paper was folded up tight inside and when I opened it up and spread it out on the floor in front of me I could see it was a copy of a photo – God only knows how they managed to take it – which had captured a scene that made me quiver with anxiety. I arched my back involuntarily as I gawped at the shot of five fat rats feasting on a banquet of rich food – caviar, oysters, branded House of Commons chocolate, rum and raisin ice cream, and a mountain of cheese slices piled high above their heads. The rats had posed for a group shot with their arms round one another, drunk on the food they had ingested, like a bunch of lads at the end of the first night of a particularly hedonistic stag weekend. It was nauseating, but the truly horrifying realization was that all this had taken place in the heart of No 10, in DC's flat upstairs.

The picture had been taken while the rats – and the food – were rolling around in the Camerons' bathtub, the very same bath I perch on most mornings while DC prepares for the day ahead, and I could see the boss's shaving mirror in the background. The date and time were printed clearly on the sheet – Friday 18 March at 9.30 a.m. So they'd thrown their big celebration a few hours after the boss and I had chewed the cud. And they'd done so deliberately to prove that nowhere is out of bounds and there is no part of No 10 they can't infest at will, regardless of whether it's darkest night or broad daylight.

Perhaps this job is just too big, but if I ask for help it could be curtains for me. Worse still, I could see this picture being leaked and ending up all over the papers. Professional failure is one thing, but public humiliation is quite another.

So I grabbed the photo hurriedly and shot out of the room, running back to the comfort of my Kate and Wills cushion. Except this time it didn't feel so comfortable – I could have sworn the happy couple were scowling back at me, and the longer I looked at their pictures, the deeper their frowns became.

Saturday 19 March

DC says there are very few perks in this job, but I came across a cupboard stuffed full of them this morning. I was scouting around in the basement trying to find a good place for a catnap when I found it.

I managed to prize the door open and saw that the

shelves were crammed full of bric-à-brac: an old Persian rug, loosely rolled, lay across a bottle of whisky and a wicker hamper on the bottom shelf, and further up I thought I could make out a china bowl, turned on its side, squeezed into a space beneath a picture frame resting on a jewellery box.

I tugged at a glistening silver necklace, first with one paw, and then with two, until – finally – it came loose, bringing all the other stuff tumbling out of the cupboard along with it.

I counted two rugs, either of which would look quite fetching in the Terracotta Room, three graphite tennis racquets, a bottle of whisky, a picnic hamper and a clutch of colourful ties. A piece of paper attached to the racquets had a message from Nicolas Sarkozy scrawled on it, and one of the carpets was from the manager of the Taj Mahal Hotel in Delhi.

The whisky was a present from Francis Rossi, the bloke out of Status Quo, according to the gift tag, and the hamper full of food had been sent by Kelly Hoppen, the interior designer. She must have heard Sam was having the No 11 flat tarted up and decided to angle for some work.

DC heard all about my little adventure, of course. I've realized it's impossible to keep a secret in this place.

'What on earth were you doing rummaging through my little box of tricks?' DC asked me this evening.

'Looking for rats,' I lied. 'I think you'll find it's in my job description.'

For a second I thought I could see Dave's relaxed demeanour slipping.

'Sorry boss,' I said, 'it's just that things haven't been going too well.'

'Don't worry,' DC said, 'you're far less trouble than the rest of them.'

'By the way,' he added, 'you do know I'm just keeping that stuff safe on behalf of the nation?'

'Good on you, Dave,' I said. 'If the Blairs had got hold of it, Cherie would have had it straight on eBay.'

Sunday 20 March

I can't help thinking Harriet is taking her job as a handler a little too literally. She grabbed me by the scruff of the neck today and announced we were on the move.

I'm down in the basement now, on the same floor as the staff canteen, which suits me fine. If you follow the big winding staircase all the way down to the very bottom stop and walk to the end of a long corridor, there's a door which opens on to a patio beneath the Downing Street garden. That's where my basket sits.

My Kate and Wills cushion is looking a bit the worse for wear, and it's not exactly the Dorchester when it comes to the fixtures and fittings, but I've got pretty much everything I need. The Special Branch guys who are based down here have fixed up a big scratching post for me with a ball fixed to the top with elastic. As far as I can tell, those boys have got bugger all else to do.

There's no cat flap – the plods insist it's a security risk. But there's a room full of secretarial staff next door, in an office that overlooks No 10's backyard and they are pretty good at opening the door for me so I can get out. The women who work there are called the 'garden girls' on account of the view they have – it's the name Churchill gave them during the war, although to be frank a fair few of them are of an age when they should probably be thinking about retirement.

The thing is none of them are in a hurry to leave because they get to go to some exotic places.

At least one of them has to travel with the boss at all times in case he wants to dictate a letter or get hold of someone important, even when he goes on holiday. So back in the Blair years they would end up getting free trips to Cliff Richard's holiday home in Barbados and Berlusconi's Sardinian villa.

Admittedly under Gordon it wasn't quite as glamorous, but a free week in Southwold is still not to be sniffed at. It's just down the road from Aldeburgh, where they have all that classical music, and the toffs love a bit of that, don't they?

DC's a bit nervous about looking out of touch with ordinary voters, so the furthest the garden girls have got since he stepped through that shiny black door is Cornwall.

The garden girls moan about it all the time, but the boss can't keep up his 'man of the people' act for much longer. Sunnier climes surely await. The door by my basket opens on to the Rose Garden, and on the right-hand side there's an area called the Freddie Flintoff Memorial Flower-bed, where the petunias seem to grow a little taller. Apparently the erstwhile England cricket captain had been invited to No 10 in 2005 after their Ashes win. There'd been some pretty robust celebrating the night before and Freddie, somewhat bleary-eyed, couldn't find the toilet, so he relieved himself on the petunias instead. If I'd been around back then he could have used my litter tray.

Monday 21 March

I heard Nick describe his office as 'palatial' today. He was on the blower to some *apparatchik* or other, with his feet up on his desk. 'I know, I know,' he was joking. 'And the last place wasn't big enough to swing a cat in!'

Nicky saw me out of the corner of his eye, coughed conspicuously and sat bolt upright, phone still in hand.

'Anyway, no more excuses,' he barked into the mouthpiece. 'Just action that immediately, will you?' What a plonker.

He placed the dog and bone back in its cradle and eyed me suspiciously.

'What can I do for you, er, Larry?' he asked, shuffling over towards the doorway where I was sat and bending down to scratch me under my chin. Everyone in this place knows I can't get enough of that, but I hadn't forgotten our first encounter, so I stood my ground.

After a little while, he undid my collar and placed it in the palm of his hand, turning it over and over and muttering something about 'bugs' all the while.

I thought he was on about fleas, but eventually the penny dropped – Nicky thinks I'm spying for DC. The boy has finally lost his marbles. I suppose it would be easy enough to fit a tiny microphone on to my collar, and it wouldn't be too hard for DC to get his hands on one, either. If he doesn't trust MI5 (and who does?) he only has to give his old mate Rebekah a call and borrow some of the *News of the World*'s surveillance gear.

I slunk out after Clegg had replaced my collar, but the whole thing got me thinking.

Nicky's had a tough twelve months, and it's made him slightly paranoid, but I could do worse than hook up some micro-cameras to those rats myself so I could track their movements, David Attenborough style.

The problem is I'd have to get close to the buggers first.

One of the garden girls fetched up with a little toy mouse she'd knitted over the weekend today, an odd-looking creature with a shock of black hair and a red rosette pinned to his chest. Downing Street had been told by one of my old warders at Battersea Dogs & Cats Home that I was always playing with a fake rubber rat when I was a resident of SW11 and she'd taken it upon herself to make me a replacement. He's called 'Milimouse', and I've been clawing and gnawing at him all afternoon. If only it was as easy to corner a real rodent.

Tuesday 22 March – morning

The canteen has seen a few changes since DC and his lot arrived, or so Harriet claims. Hilton made sure there was granola and yoghurts served alongside the bacon and fried eggs of a morning, for a start.

There are some strange things going on down here, though. Computer terminals are dotted amongst the tables and chairs, and every time I come in here to zigzag through the table legs in search of leftovers, brushing affectionately past calves and ankles, at least two shiny-faced advisors are bashing away at key-boards.

I can't be sure why they don't use the computers at their own desks, but I can hazard a bloody good guess.

Dirty tricks are best carried out face to face, but if emails are involved, it's a good idea to use a computer that doesn't require a log-in.

They used to worry about paper trails in Whitehall, but electronic trails are far more difficult to hide.

Tuesday 22 March – afternoon

DC announced this afternoon that Boy George had magicked up a 100 million quid to spend on potholes. That's what happens around here: you put your hand down the back of the settee and find a few million quid. It's all good news as far as I'm concerned. With all those rats about, the fewer holes we have the better.

Perhaps some of it *will* actually be spent on the roads. They're starting to tart Whitehall up already, with one eye on next month's wedding no doubt.

No one's expecting a fairy tale this time, not like back in the day when Diana married Charles; the nation was a little more credulous back then. It seems like it's going to be a good day out, although Kate has got what Olly would call a 'good back-story'. It's not exactly rags-to-riches material, but it turns out her ancestors are from the north-east. Her granddad was a miner in Durham and some of her relatives are still up in that neck of the woods. Just wait till those rats find out. They'll be claiming squatters' rights!

Wednesday 23 March

Budget day. Boy George got his brand new red box out this morning and displayed it for all to see on the steps of No 11.* I watched it all unfold on Sky News, but I couldn't help thinking not much has changed since Cameron and Boy George took the reins.

No wonder Ken Clarke, the old fella with the Hush Puppies, fell asleep halfway through George's speech.

Booze went up, and fags went up, like they have every year, although Georgie boy was clever enough to slice a few pence off a gallon of petrol.

I reckon the Chancellor's been overdoing his vocal exercises, because he had a frog in his throat this afternoon. Luckily he'd managed to smuggle one of his servants into the chamber, a young guy with red hair who sat on the bench beside DC and reached over to

---

* It turned out later that Boy George's box cost £4,300 to make. That seems a bit steep when you consider how skint the country is. Sam could have got Smythson to knock one up for less.

pour water into his glass at critical moments. (At least I think it was water: George has what DC refers to as 'a colourful past' so I couldn't swear to it.)

It was only much later, when the red-haired man turned up at No 10, that I realized he wasn't a servant at all. I was warming myself up against the radiator in the lobby when I heard DC introduce him to Mrs C as Danny Alexander, a former park ranger who now helps George with his sums.

'I tell you what,' I said to the boss after he'd left. 'Ministers are getting younger these days. That Danny fella looks like he rides a BMX into the Treasury.'

'Oh, don't worry about him,' DC said. 'He's a bit like that ornament on the mantelpiece.'

'How do you mean?'

'Just for show.'

A bit like the rest of the Lib Dems, I reckon.

Thursday 24 March

There are two big rooms on the ground floor within a few paces of DC's Den. Hilton and his team are based in one of them, diagonally opposite the boss's hideout.

Boy George calls them 'blue sky thinkers', but I've never seen them in action, so I took the liberty of inviting myself in this afternoon, scratching at the heavy wooden door until one of Hilton's advisors opened up.

He stood there gawping, one hand gripping the door handle, until I let out a 'meow' and he looked down to see me sitting at his feet.

'Bloody cat,' he said, pushing me away with his foot.

Then a quiet voice drifted out of the room.

'The cat is welcome here,' it said.

Hilton's advisor sighed and ushered me into the office. His boss was positioned on a chair in the lotus position in the middle of the room, surrounded by five smartly dressed advisors sat on the floor.

'Sit with us a while, cat,' he said, pointing to the carpet. I did as I was told. A murmur of appreciation went around the room.

'We play games, cat,' Hilton said.

Do you now? I thought. 'I've heard all about the sort of games you Svengali types get up to.'

I'm not sure what was making me more uncomfortable: Hilton's voice, which sounded light enough to float out of the open window behind him, or the fact he wasn't wearing any socks or shoes.

'We play mind games,' Hilton continued.

'Yeah, you and John Lennon, mate,' I said.

Hilton made out like he hadn't heard me.

'You don't understand,' Hilton said. 'We like intellectual challenges, cat. We play games of mental dexterity.'

'OK, I'm in,' I said. 'Activate the cube!'

The girl sat furthest away from Hilton laughed into her tissue.

'What was that?' Hilton said, frowning.

He got up from his seat. 'I'm sensing some negative energy, cat,' he said, moving menacingly towards me. 'You can't build a Big Society with negative energy, man.'

Strewth, we've got a right one here, I thought.

'Cat,' I said. 'I'm a cat.' And I legged it out of there sharpish.

Friday 25 March

It's a bit dark and gloomy down in the basement. Perfect conditions for those rats to skulk around in. I expect that's why they put me down here.

It can be slightly spooky at times. When I woke up this morning the only sound I could hear was the low hum of the three imposing vending machines which stand on each side of the corridor close to where the Special Branch guys sit. They look like they're protecting the rooms where the cops spend all day sitting around, like the sentries with the bearskin hats who stand guard outside the Palace. I call them the Goldilocks machines because along with the cans of pop, McCoy's crisps and microwaveable meals on offer, they also sell porridge. Well, there was a Scotsman in charge a few years back, after all.

Nicky and DC were filmed taking questions from the public up in Nottingham today and Nick forgot to take his microphone off. 'If we keep doing this, we won't find anything to bloody disagree on in the bloody TV debates,' he told DC as they walked off stage. Remember 'I agree with Nick'? Well, who would have believed back then that Nick agreed with Dave?

Saturday 26 March

It was carnage 'up west' today.

There was a big march through central London to protest against the public-sector cuts.

I watched it all unfold live on Sky News. Ed Miliband was there, but so were the usual bunch of troublemakers and I, for one, was expecting it to kick off.

Sure enough, it all got a bit tasty in the afternoon at about the time I should have been polishing off my tinned tuna. Only there was no one about to dish out my grub.

They were all glued to the telly watching a gang of

blokes wearing balaclavas smash the windows of a Porsche showroom in Park Lane.

The Ritz Hotel on Piccadilly was the next to be targeted. Sam Cam sat in the Den in silence shaking her head but DC didn't seem to give a monkey's.

'We've had the Arab Spring and the Jasmine Revolution,' he scoffed. 'What's this one going to be called – the afternoon tea and cucumber sandwiches uprising?'

I was a bit nervous they'd head down this way, but the crowd stopped off at Trafalgar Square. A separate load of protestors staged a sit-in at Fortnum & Mason on Piccadilly. Apparently, they're furious because its owners don't pay enough tax. Sam once described Fortnum's as a food shop that's even pricier than Waitrose: apparently only upper-class types who don't want to traipse around a supermarket with a trolley can afford to shop there.

'Too posh to push,' I think Sam once called them.

Anyway, the old dears down at Fortnum's looked a bit confused. They were probably wondering what all the fuss was about. You don't expect to get caught up in a riot when you pop out for a £4.75 jar of piccalilli, do you?

Late tonight, before I retired for the evening, DC was moaning about the cost of sweeping up all that shattered glass and cleaning off the graffiti. I may have been pushing my luck, but I couldn't resist reminding him he's got form when it comes to smashing up private property.

'I'm not being funny, Dave, but you and your Oxford mates did a pretty good job on that restaurant up in Oxford when you were in that Bit of a Bully club.'

'Bullingdon Club,' he replied, wearily. 'And it was a long time ago. Besides, we paid for the damage.'

'Only coz you could afford to, mate,' I thought.

Sunday 27 March

I spent half the morning gazing out at the garden from a window-sill on the first-floor landing, half asleep, watching the birds hop from tree to tree.

It's funny to think that this time last year I was out there in my natural habitat, padding around Battersea Park, frightening the squirrels and sleeping rough. Now I'm seeing how the other half lives. Mrs C has even forked out for a personal trainer who puts the stars through their paces; people you only ever see on the front page of *Now!* magazine, such as Mel C and Sting's missus, Trudie Styler.

Don't take this personal, like, but you humans are an odd bunch. Imagine paying someone to run around the pavements with you. Watching Sam sprinting down Downing Street put me in mind of my old mate Smudge, the tomcat I used to hang about with before we both got lifted and stuck in that cat motel down SW11 way. We had the run of the streets, me and Smudge.

What DC and his lot don't appreciate is it's not easy to train a free spirit like me to be a miserable old rat-catcher. I've always made my own rules and, until now, I've never worked a day in my life – not that I'd want DC to know that.

I'm not one to whinge, or get sentimental about old times, but life's not what it used to be. I may have had to scavenge and scour bins when I was on the streets, and steer well clear of foxes, but I could bed down wherever I chose. I wasn't 'The Downing Street Cat', or 'Joe' or 'Larry'. I was just me. Now I've got to be on guard all the time, expected to become a surveillance expert and hand out justice to rodents. If you think about it, it's a bit like being Old Bill. And that thought makes me very uncomfortable.

Ed Miliband was up in Nottingham today talking about the 'squeezed middle'. I could tell him all he needs to know about that. I've lost count of the number of times I've been scooped up and mollycoddled since I arrived here.

Monday 28 March

Nick's office is in an imposing-looking building called the Cabinet Office, which has an entrance around the corner on Whitehall, a few steps away from the Cenotaph. I think Nicky boy prefers to use the grander No 10 entrance. Well, he would do, wouldn't he?

Nick still likes to say he's only a few steps away from the most powerful man in the country. Technically, he's right. But now I'm on the inside I know he's being 'disingenuous'. It's a long word the scribblers use when they don't want to risk using a shorter one beginning with 'l'.

If you exit DC's Den there is a short staircase, which isn't quite long enough to stretch to the first floor. It heads west towards the Cabinet Office, where Cleggy sits. There used to be a door linking the two, only you can't walk down there now without going through a security gate that everyone has to negotiate.

They call it 'Checkpoint Charlie' – or at least that's the name Boy George and DC have given it – and it's a bugger to get through.

You have to step into a soundproof plastic tube, which closes around you and opens up on the other side. It's like a scene out of *Star Trek*, and DC always cracks the same bad joke when Clegg steps in: 'Beam me up, Nicky.'

It can take a while to get from one side to the other, particularly if there's a good old-fashioned British queue forming along the corridor.

I've seen Nick standing patiently in line, allowing

lift engineers and press offices to pass through with a nod of the head, while his clenched fists get tighter and his smile grows stiffer.

When DC walks through Checkpoint Charlie the Whitehall waves part to let him pass, and as he bounds up the steps, two by two, one of his security men speaks into a microphone pinned to his lapel: 'The boss is on the move,' he says, and the plastic tube opens up remotely before the boss has even got to it. No pass required.

That told me all I needed to know about the partnership between DC and Cleggy.

Tuesday 29 March

I thought the only people who were allowed to ask politicians questions were old blokes in suits with public-school accents called Paxman or Dimbleby.

So I nearly fell off my cushion this evening when that Fiona Bruce sort announced on the news that some old dear called Gillian Duffy had collared Nicky Boy in Rochdale and given him a right earful. Apparently she did the same thing to Gordon Brown last year.

He didn't have the best of luck, old Gordy. The moment he told us all he'd abolished boom and bust, the global financial system collapsed and he had to rip up his golden rule.

Now Mrs Duffy's a minor celebrity. She does talk some sense, to be fair, and I can almost see ITV offering her a talk show. (She'd be a lot more palatable than Piers Morgan. There's nothing worse than a scribbler who gets a sniff of success.)

DC and Sam were drinking large G&Ts in the Downing Street garden this evening, making the most of the lighter nights now the clocks have gone forward, when one of the teenage helpers rushed out to tell them Nick had been Duffed up. The boss couldn't stop laughing, telling Sam Cam that Mrs T would have been proud of the handbagging Duffy had administered. And there's me thinking the two of them were meant to be on the same side.

'Duffy?' Sam repeated absent-mindedly. 'Hmmm . . . I don't mind some of her early stuff.' DC gulped his G&T down in one.

Wednesday 30 March

Wasn't it DC who said he wanted to see an end to 'Punch and Judy politics' a few years back?

I only ask because I got to see my first Prime Minister's Questions today and it had more punch than an Amir Khan fight.

I ventured out again, but this time I hitched a lift, jumping in the back of DC's car as it pulled off to make the short journey down the road to Parliament. He was so absorbed in his reading material he didn't even notice I was there.

Facing one another across the floor of the House of Commons, DC kicked things off by congratulating Ed Miliband on the announcement that he's getting hitched to his partner Justine. All very civilized, I thought.

But then it got slightly rowdy. As he did his best to answer question after question, the other Ed sat next to Miliband – Balls, I think he's called – yapped away like a barking dog. It took me right back to my days at Battersea, where you couldn't reach the end of a sentence without your words being drowned out by a chorus of howls and cat-calls.

And then Dave lost it. 'I wish the Shadow Chancellor would shut up,' he said. 'I may be alone in thinking him the most annoying person in British politics.'

'I thought that was David Davis,' I whispered to myself. 'Or so you're always telling me.'

A member of Her Majesty's press was sat a bit further up the same bench, notebook and pen in hand. He shot me a strange look, so I jumped to the floor and scarpered.

'Don't quote me on that,' I whispered on the way out.

The scribbler glanced at me again, shook his head, and carried on scribbling.

Thursday 31 March

DC and his helpers have come up with a new three-word curse: 'Bloody Andrew Lansley.'

I asked around and it turns out Lansley's the silver-haired guy who runs all the hospitals. I think he has some big changes planned but the voters aren't too happy about them, and nor are some of Nicky's crowd.

DC once told me there are three organizations in this country no politician can ever touch – the NHS, the BBC and the Royal Family. The Tories did say something about 'no more pointless NHS reorganizations' in their manifesto, but Lansley only wants to carry out some minor surgery, as far as I can tell. But even that's enough to make DC jumpy.

'Bloody Andrew Lansley,' he said, when Lansley popped up on Sky News trying to explain what he's up to. He said it again an hour later when he dropped a stapler on his foot.

Every Tuesday, DC holds a meeting with all his top people in the room with the big table next door to his office. I like to pop along whenever I can to pick up some gossip.

As they all filed out the other day, one grey man turned to another grey man and said: 'You do know Andrew's going to be "Spelmaned"?'

Sounds pretty nasty, doesn't it?

APRIL 2011

Wednesday 1 April*

DC has a sign on his desk which reads, 'We're all in this together', only some of us are in it deeper than others, if you ask me.

I've been doing some digging on those rats – there's a file on each of them in that cabinet in DC's office – and it seems to me they are up to their necks in the brown stuff. And I'm not talking about Newcastle Brown Ale.

Most people are tightening their belts at the moment, but some people had bigger waists to start with, if you get my meaning.

Boy George and his mates probably think an economy drive is leaving the Jag at home and taking the Volkswagen Golf to the shops instead.

There are some disaffected types around the

---

* DC got me good and proper this morning. 'Have you heard the news?' he asked. 'The Queen's going to write her autobiography! She told me at the Palace this morning that she's signed a £10 million deal with HarperCollins.'

'Isn't that one of Gramps's companies?' I said. 'I thought those two didn't see eye to eye?'

DC laughed. 'Have a butcher's at your notebook,' he replied. 'And check what day it is.' Very droll, I'm sure.

country, what with the economy hobbling along and the cuts starting to bite, but let's be honest, some places are suffering more than others. Plenty of them are losing their jobs: teachers, council workers, pen-pushers in magistrates' courts, coppers. Even soldiers could be signing on before long.

Now, I've got no time for scroungers, but it seems to me that King Rat has brought his band of reprobates down here because a few of them were struggling to find a way to make ends meet on their home turf.

They did what that old-timer Lord Tebbit said they should do: got on their proverbial bikes and went out looking for work. DC calls them squatters. They would call themselves 'economic migrants'. I call them a pain in the backside, quite frankly. But there's a part of me that feels we really ought to be on the same side.

Saturday 2 April

DC is going on tour with Andrew Lansley. I don't think Take That have got anything to worry about.

Officially, they want to reassure the public about the NHS changes Lansley wants to push through. Unofficially, I'd say the whole idea's gone a bit Pete Tong and Lansley's one vote of confidence away from the sack.

Oliver drafted a press release with the boss today saying it's time to 'pause, listen, reflect and improve'. I told him that sounds like the sort of nonsense Hilton comes out with.

The scribblers are already writing that DC is preparing the ground for another U-turn, although there are no royal wedding invitations to be gained by caving in to doctors and nurses, as far as I'm aware, so I reckon DC will stay the course.

Cameron and Lansley will start their nationwide 'listening tour' next week. It's the sort of occasion I'd do anything to avoid – like bath-time and the terrible day that vet took a blade to my whatsits. I suspect DC feels much the same way, but there's a lot at stake.

Forests are one thing, but he also had to scrap a plan to stop giving out school milk last year and he's already dumped proposals to slash school sports budgets.

The awkward squad crack open another bottle of champers on the Commons terrace each time DC gets in a bit of a tangle and he can't afford to make many more slip-ups.

I was having a doze on Kate and Wills this evening when I started to think about DC's situation. Perhaps I can learn a bit from the way these politicians operate. I wonder if it might be time for me to pause, listen and reflect, and strike some sort of deal with those rodents. One thing's for sure; I don't think I'm going to beat them using poison and rat traps.

Sunday 3 April

One of DC's speechwriters was in today so she could get on with some work and she had the nerve to complain I ponged a bit. I'm not being funny, sweetheart, but have you tried getting up at the crack of dawn and putting in a few hours' graft before breakfast?

I've been honing my skills, you see, sneaking out early and doing a little bit of 'target practice' in the No 10 Rose Garden. There are plenty of birds to stalk out there and the truth is they're a lot easier to get hold of than those bleeding rats. These rodents are so quick on their feet they make Speedy Gonzalez look like Bagpuss.

There's another slight hitch an' all. I'm not what you'd call a 'natural born killer', despite what that lot down at the cats' home told No 10 over the phone. It's a 100 years or more since my ancestors had to catch vermin on a regular basis, after all, and my instincts have been dulled over the generations. You lot are partly to blame. If you keep feeding us Sheba, why bother hunting for food? We cats are no mugs, after all.

Monday 4 April – afternoon

DC is planning to whisk Mrs C away for a few days in the Med later this week.

It was meant to be a surprise but she's obviously got wind of it and I think she might be thinking about squeezing into her swimsuit. She scowled at DC at lunchtime when the boss pushed a cheese sandwich in her direction.

'Oh God, not for me,' Sam said, patting her tummy repeatedly. 'No carbs before Marbs.'

DC looked confused. 'What on earth are you talking about?' he asked.

'No carbohydrates before Marbella,' Sam explained. It's a phrase she's picked up from *The Only Way Is Essex*, the reality show that all the female humans rave about. There are so many channels these days, and so many hours to fill, that almost anyone can have their own show.

I've thought about pitching a fly-on-the-wall documentary about myself before now, but I know the boss would kibosh it. He wouldn't want more cameramen than usual crawling all over No 10.

I don't think the boss can keep up with all Sam's fads and her changing telly tastes (he's a busy man after all).

'Where do you find these catchphrases?' he asked her today over the lunch table.

'TOWIE,' Sam replied.

'Towie? Is that one of your Notting Hill friends you haven't told me about?'

'No, no, no. It's short for *The Only Way Is Essex*,' Sam said, looking ever so slightly exasperated. 'It's a TV show.'

'Oh I see!' the PM said. 'I think I'll stick to *Made in Chelsea*.'

He's full of surprises, the boss.

Monday 4 April

Nick Clegg's bedroom door was ajar this evening so I popped my head around to say hello.

He was sat cross-legged on his bed staring up at the space above the headboard where the Colin Firth poster used to be Sellotaped to the wall, tears streaming down his face.

His Sky Digibox was tuned to VH1 and a song was blaring out of the portable TV balanced on the old oak chair by the side of his bed. I recognized the tune immediately: 'Toxic' by Britney Spears. Nicky's clearly taking the lyrics a bit personal.

He often sits alone in his room these days crying to music. The other week he was curled on the floor with his yellow quilt cover wrapped around him sobbing to 'Money's Too Tight to Mention' – and he's not even a big Mick Hucknall fan.

The problem is Nicky hasn't been the most popular kid in school since he abandoned his old mates to knock around with DC, and getting the cold shoulder can be tough to take at that age.

I snuck out of there as quietly as I could.

I wish for his sake I could have shut the door behind me, but sometimes four paws are no match for two hands.

'The First Cut Is the Deepest' started playing. Nicky's sobs grew louder.

Tuesday 5 April

I've been trying to get my head around this 'alternative vote' nonsense everyone's banging on about. DC and Nicky have been arguing about it so much they've abandoned the happy couple act they used to put on for the cameras and started rowing about it in public. I know DC doesn't want to change the system we use for voting, but the rest of it is all a bit confusing. Nick agrees with Ed Miliband, who agrees with Alan Johnson, and DC agrees with Boy George, who both agree with two old Labour guys the scribblers call 'grey beards', John Reid and David Blunkett. (I don't know how they pass their journalism degrees: only one of them has a beard, and it isn't grey.)

I'm not sure who to believe: DC wants to keep 'first past the post' and Nicky boy would like voters to rank candidates, with their favourite first and their least favourite last. If I'm right, the AV-ers want to make votes for your second favourite party count for something at election time, but DC says the party who come second could actually end up finishing first. It's all as clear as mud, but Boy George told me AV is a bit like cheering for your second favourite team to win the FA Cup. I haven't got a second favourite team – it's Chelsea or bust – so I think we should stick with what we've got.

Wednesday 6 April

Their bags are packed.

The staff are excited because the boss is off for a few days. Samantha is excited because she's getting DC to herself – a special treat for her 40th birthday.

She's been talking about 'hitting the big four-O' for a while now, although I have a sneaky feeling she'd hoped to be celebrating in a slightly more glamorous location.

They are flying to Spain in something called 'cattle class' on an airline called Ryanair. Perhaps the geezer who runs it gives money to the Tory party because the garden girls swear they've always used BA in the past.

'Who'd have thought we'd be flying Chav Air to the Med?' Sam said, laughing as they sat in the lobby this afternoon waiting for their car to Stanstead.

DC dropped his copy of *The Times* to the floor.

'How many times do I have to tell you NEVER to use the "C" word, Samantha?' he asked.

There's a long list of words beginning with 'c' that were banned by a bloke called Andy Coulson, an old employee of Gramps who worked at Downing Street for a while. He left under a cloud but all the staff still rave about him.

Coulson used to keep all the journalists in check, just like Olly does now, and DC says I would have liked him – although apparently he's a Spurs fan so I'm not so sure.

In any case, Coulson's 'C list' is still stuck to the door of Sam's SMEG fridge:

Council estate – to be used sparingly
Class – avoid wherever possible
Comprehensive school – mention only in context
    of rapidly improving educational standards
Chav – completely off limits

Sam rolled her eyes. 'Here's another 'C' word for you, DC,' she said. 'Chillax.'

'I beg your pardon?'

'Chillax,' she repeated, slowly this time. 'You know ... chill out? Relax?'

DC looked confused

'Oh, never mind,' Sam said, from behind her over-sized Gucci shades.

Thursday 7 April

I decided to pay Ted and Harold another early morning visit. I caught up on a bit of sleep first, mind, because I'd been up half the night on a reconnaissance mission to the Houses of Parliament. I've got a plan, you see, but if I'm going to put it into action I'll need to persuade those rats to come to the negotiating table. And that means I have to find them first.

DC told me last night very few wars end without the two sides talking to one another eventually. I think his mind was on Afghanistan, but he may as well have been talking about my tussle with the awkward squad.

I pushed the security room door open and found Ted perched on his chair, dipping a HobNob into his cuppa.

He tried to feed me some melted chocolate buttons he found in his trouser pocket, but I turned my nose up at them: I've put on a few pounds since I fetched up here, and that isn't a good look when you're meant to be racing around the place eradicating vermin.

Ted has been keeping an eye on those monitors and he reckons the rats have a daily routine, taking it in turns to travel in twos to the bins out back to scavenge for food. He says they slide out of a drainpipe of a morning faster than Dominique Strauss-Kahn legging it out of a New York hotel room.

They land on a pile of black bin bags piled up against the wall and start sifting through them. About half an hour later, they turn up on another monitor, dragging carrier bags full of food into an attic room at the top of the house.

'You watch,' Ted said, pressing a button on the control panel in front of him. 'They'll turn up there any second now.'

And so they did, one of them pulling faces at the camera, the other too busy munching on an apple core to care. 'I'll put the kettle on,' Ted said, but I'd already turned on my heels and legged it up to the fourth floor. I got there just as they were on their way out.

I thought the attic where I cornered the rats was the room Gramps stays in when he's in town, but perhaps DC and Sam have moved him to more salubrious surroundings. It's now an office kitted out with what looks like a mini telephone exchange.

This must be where the famous Downing Street switchboard is based. I heard DC and Osborne talking about how they wanted to move it up here to free up some space a while ago. The switchboard operators can track anyone down, wherever they are in the world, at any time, but they must have been on a break when I raced up there. It's lucky there wasn't an international incident this morning, because DC would have ended up using his mobile to get hold of Ban Ki-moon.

The rats looked petrified, cowering in the corner. I

worried for a minute that one of them was going to go for my neck, but I remembered I was wearing my smart new collar, which would have protected me from their sharp little teeth.

'Look fellas,' I began, holding up a paw. 'Just hold on a minute and listen to me. I know you've had the run of the place for months, but it doesn't seem like you've learned much about how politics works. Dave and the rest of the humans are using this old tactic called "divide and rule". But if we joined forces instead of being at each other's throats then we could all get ourselves a much better deal.'

They still looked a bit nervous, but I could see their ears were twitching and they were obviously listening. 'It works like this ... all the blokes with power – that's the government, and my boss – set us ordinary fellas against each other while they rule the roost. Think how much power we'd have if we learned to get along and help each other out instead of falling for their tactics.'

I kept talking and used every trick in the book to calm them down. You learn how to handle these situations out on the streets. I let them know I could be a friend and not a foe, and by the time they shuffled off back to wherever the rest of them were hiding we'd arranged to meet out front for a summit on Friday 15 April.

I'm not one to blow my own trumpet, but the Pied Piper of Hamlyn himself couldn't have charmed those rats more effectively than I did.

Friday 8 April

If you want a private natter at No 10, or even just a moment to yourself, you have to escape outside.

DC can take a stroll in the garden, where even the most sneaky reporters can't earwig, but anyone who smokes – and a few who don't – leaves the building by the front door and walks to the end of Downing Street, taking a small set of steps which lead to the rear exit of the No 10 car park.

I go there occasionally to get away from it all.

The Rose Garden is all too often crowded with schoolchildren attending one of Mrs C's receptions – I'm usually spotted by the teachers first, but they all make a right fuss of me – and I could do without the drama.

You have to run the gauntlet out front, especially if a celebrity has dropped in to see DC. It's a bit like stepping on to the red carpet at a film premiere at Leicester Square, with dozens of cameras flashing.

Those big, furry grey microphones lie in wait an' all, poised to be thrust into unsuspecting faces. They look like oversized rodents, those microphones, and I always jump out of my skin when I see them lying around on the pavement outside the big black door.

I was standing on the car park steps this evening, shading myself from the sun, when I noticed a dozen or so Downing Street staff standing in a corner on the tarmac in a huddle, surrounding a ginger-haired geezer wearing a rugby shirt and deck shoes.

'That's strange,' I thought. 'The blokes in this place usually dress quite dapper.'

I thought they were smoking and chatting away, at first, but then I saw not a single one of them had lit up, and it looked like they were staring at something the ginger-haired fella was holding up for them to read. I was too far away to get a proper butcher's, but I thought I recognized him from the IT department. Just as I was about to take a better look, a silver Audi came screeching into the car park and slid to a halt, stopping just short of the crowd of staffers.

A bloke with a plummy accent barked something at the kid in the rugby top and he jumped into the passenger seat. The Audi sped off again, reversing at speed through the car park exit, while the two blokes on security stood there open-mouthed. (I tell you what; they don't half make some decent cars, those Germans.)

I've been racking my tiny brain ever since, but I still can't place that redhead. But I can smell something fishy, and it's definitely not my tea.

Saturday 9 April

They're back from Spain already. I was sat on a second-floor window-sill, watching the snappers and scribblers in the street below chattering, smoking and swapping stories, when the Jag pulled up outside.

I ran down the stairs and into the reception area, slipping on the tiles, just as Sam stumbled through the door. She dropped her leather Oliver Bonas bag to the floor with a thud and exhaled loudly as she leaned back against the wall.

'I never thought I'd be glad to be back here!' she said.

DC was right behind her, struggling under the weight of two suitcases, a Marks & Sparks holdall, a laptop and a sombrero.

It sounds like they didn't get a moment's rest.

'God! It was awful,' said Sam. 'They were outside the hotel before we arrived. It was like they knew we were coming.'

Cameron spotted me gazing up at him and bent down to scratch my chin. 'That's the last time we go to Granada,' he sighed.

'I thought you'd been to the Med?' I said. 'Please tell me you did the *Coronation Street* tour?'

Sam suppressed a snigger. 'Oh, Larry, what are we going to do with you?'

Sunday 10 April

I ran into Boy George this evening on a balcony attached to one of the No 11 rooms, which overlooks the Downing Street garden, looking pensive and puffing on a cigar. He's giving up the fags, but perhaps he thinks Havanas will give him that gravelly voice he's after. He'll never get to be PM sounding like Mickey Mouse on helium.

I wonder if George ever stands there, as he was tonight, looking at the lights from No 10 and wondering how long DC intends to hang around. At least ten years, would be my guess, and possibly a lot longer than that. (Long enough to see me out, in any case.)

I sat in silence for a few minutes until I plucked up the courage to ask him if it was true.

'Is what true?' he said, his voice sounding squeakier than usual.

'That you stopped Hunt getting the ballroom dancer's job.'

A few months before I pitched up at No 10, a couple of scribblers from the *Daily Telegraph* caused a right kerfuffle by posing as voters and secretly recording a chat with Vince Cable, the Lib Dem Business Secretary who does a bit of ballroom dancing in his spare time and fancies himself as a bit of a mover and shaker.

Cable had a pop at Gramps, telling them he'd 'declared war' on his papers and that he'd probably win. That didn't go down too well with the old fella, as you can imagine, and the rumour is Hunt was lined up to replace Cable – only Boy George here thinks Hunt has his eye on the top job and told the boss he couldn't wear it. So the entire plan was shelved.

'You might have heard that,' Osborne said, when I put it to him. 'I couldn't possibly comment.'

I told him I thought Hunt was overrated.

'He won't last long,' he said, smiling.

'When are you going to finish him off?' I said, half joking.

'2012,' he replied, flicking his cigar ash into the bushes below. 'Straight after the Olympics.'

'Surely he'll be harder to get rid of by then?' I said. Hunt is in charge of sport as well as culture and it's his job to make sure London puts on a good show.

'Quite the contrary, old boy,' George said. 'If they go wrong, he'll get the blame, and if they go well, David will get all the credit.'

He dropped his cigar on the ground and stubbed it out, not with the sole of his shoe but with the heel. He may resemble one of those choir boys at Westminster Abbey, but I wouldn't want to get on the wrong side of George. He's more like one of the prefects out of *Tom Brown's Schooldays*.

Monday 11 April

It's nearly a fortnight since the bin men last paid us a visit and the rubbish is piling up out back. No wonder the rat pack are thriving.

Refuse is a touchy subject at No 10. The colour

drains from DC's face when pictures of black bin-liners piled high on the pavements appear on the news. He even started quoting Shakespeare this morning, repeating some line about 'the winter of our discontent'. I can't for the life of me think why – after all, summer is just around the corner – but DC just shook his head dismissively when I told him to enjoy the heatwave and walked on down the corridor towards the Den.

I don't know why he's so moody. He's not the only one with problems, after all.

The rats still have the run of this place and I reckon my probationary period might not have long left to run. I'm not even certain all the cats that have done my job in the past have gone the distance, if you get my meaning.

The last moggy at this place only lasted a few months, and she arrived with a reputation as an accomplished 'mouser'. Sybil came down from Edinburgh with the last Chancellor, Alistair Darling, a Scot with a head of hair almost as white as mine, but never adjusted to life in the Big Smoke.

Before that an old fella called Humphrey, a popular cat by all accounts, was chief mouser. He was hired by Mrs Thatcher, who took one look at the annual pest control bill and fired the rat-catching firm immediately. They were charging four grand a year and Humphrey only cost a 100 quid to feed. That was Mrs T all over – always counting the pennies.

Humphrey was good at his job, too. So good, in fact, that John Major kept him on. But he was turfed out in '97, shortly after the Blairs moved in. They say Cherie didn't take to him, but I can't help thinking he might have outlived his usefulness.

Humphrey ended up seeing out his days in Cricklewood, living with one of the civil servants who used to work at No 10, or so they say. Now, I'm no snob, as you know, but I've spent most of my life in Central London and suburbia doesn't really float my boat. Besides, I always fancied retiring to the Costa del Sol. Sun, sea and sardines. What bliss.

Tuesday 12 April

DC's full of it today and all because Matt Smith gave an interview in the Currant Bun describing the boss as 'charismatic'.

'What about that, kids?' he said when they took their places at the long white marble breakfast table this morning. 'Doctor Who's a blue!'

He lobbed a copy of the paper from where he was standing by the sink and it landed in the centre of the table next to the toast rack.

'I still can't believe we have that paper in the house,' Sam Cam tutted.

Smith has been down the Commons to watch the boss in action at PMQs and told the *Sun* he reckoned he was 'polished'.

I tell you what, I wouldn't mind a natter with the Doctor myself. He'd know all about getting to grips with something that's far bigger on the inside than it looks from out front. And I could do with getting a few of those Daleks in at No 10 to exterminate these bloody rats if I need a backup plan, especially if the peace talks I arranged the other day don't go to plan.

DC was laughing with the kids this morning, telling them Nicky Clegg could be exterminated next month, until Mrs C told him to pipe down.

There are local elections in May and the Lib Dems are still doing badly in the polls. Everyone at No 10 was having good giggle today about the fact that Nicky's been taken off the Lib Dems' local election leaflets across the country (it seems his councillors think he's a bit of a liability). But then Nicky walked into the Den and everyone went quiet.

I almost feel sorry for the bloke because he's been getting it from all sides since his civil servants let it slip to the press that he won't do any work after 3 p.m. some days.

The problem is Nicky's hitched to this fiery Spanish sort called Miriam who seems to have the whip hand, if you get my drift, and she insists he has to make time for his homework.

Even DC's frightened of this Miriam sort.

Nicky isn't coping too well at the moment. The smallest row sets off the waterworks; doors get slammed, voices are raised and the occasional keyboard gets clobbered. One of the staff said today it's as if Gordon Brown never left.

Wednesday 13 April

DC must have been listening to Olly again. He was up at 5 a.m. this morning to appear on *Daybreak*, the breakfast show that's as unpopular with viewers as the Lib Dems have become with voters. It's all part of Olly's strategy to make DC come across like an ordinary family man who just happens to have an extraordinary job.

He never gets asked difficult questions on the sofa, but the viewers probably prefer a bit of light relief at that time of the morning in any case. Who wants to hear about the budget deficit when they're shovelling Cheerios into their gob and trying to get the kids off to school?

The boss was making the most of the easy ride this morning, joking that I spend all my time relaxing in the flower beds instead of chasing rats. Or at least I think he was joking.

What he doesn't properly appreciate is that I'm not just lying around sunning myself. My grey matter's working overtime and I've got those rats waiting on tenterhooks for our summit. I've come up with a plan that should work in everyone's favour.

Parliament is half empty most of the time, but No 10 is teeming. There's far more space for the rats over there than there ever will be at this place. If I can persuade them to up sticks, everyone will be happy: the rats can stay in London and I get to keep my job.

William and Kate have made a big noise about asking the couple who run the corner shop down the road from Kate's parents' house to the wedding. They invited the local butcher and the village postman an' all. Technically, of course, Kate is a commoner herself, although she's hardly what you'd call ordinary, so now the Palace is calling it the 'People's Wedding'. If that's the case, why isn't everyone invited?

Thursday 14 April

DC gave a speech on immigration today. Thank God I'm not a Siamese. It didn't go down too well with some of the cabinet – the ballroom dancer was tangoing all over the place this afternoon, muttering that it was 'very unwise' – but DC was in a great mood when he got back, crowing about how all his backbench MPs loved very word of it. Even the awkward squad are impressed.

The *Daily Mail* loved it too. Yesterday they published

an article questioning whether DC is actually a Tory. This afternoon, they were running stories on their website saying he'd delivered his best speech since the election. I can't help feeling the boss shouldn't give a monkey's either way, but politicians care far more about their press coverage than they ever let on in public.

It was only when Hilton came barging into the Den that DC stopped swaggering and started to look a little less steady on his feet. 'I thought you'd put that dog whistle away when we signed the coalition agreement,' Hilton shouted.

I've never heard anyone talk to the boss like that before.

Boy George told me later that DC had adopted a sort of code in his speech to appeal to right-wing voters. He'd used words only they'd pick up on, just like those dogs hear the high-pitched sounds a dog whistle makes when no one else can.

Still, I don't trust Boy George and all this talk about dogs make me nervous. It's bad enough with these rats running riot. The last thing I need is a canine on the loose.

Friday 15 April – morning

I had butterflies in my stomach when I woke up this morning and for a second or two I couldn't remember why. Then I glanced at my notebook and saw that today is the day of the big summit which could decide my future at No 10. But we're not scheduled to meet until this evening – assuming they even bother to turn up – so I decided to get my head down and get on with the rest of the day.

DC was complaining out loud about Craig Oliver, who can't stop banging on about 'the Westminster bubble'.

'Is that like the London Eye?' I asked DC at the breakfast table this morning. 'Sounds like one for the tourists to me.'

The boss stayed quiet and continued to spoon grapefruit into his mush in silence, then checked his watch and reached over to turn up the radio.

For some reason every set in the house is tuned to Radio 2 these days, apart from Sam's private room which is non-stop Kiss FM. It's as if the *Today* programme has been banned by royal decree.

It's all Olly's doing. He's been telling his army of spinners, and DC and Boy George too, that Radio 4 is for the chattering classes, and only people like Cameron and Miliband tune in to watch Paxo on *Newsnight* last thing at night. Perhaps he has a point; Chris Evans has nearly 9 million listeners, according to the bar chart Oliver has pinned to the wall in his office.

Sam certainly seems happier of a morning. 'Who wants to listen to John Humphrys drone on all morning?' she said today, reaching for the remote control and upping the volume.

Evans was playing a UB40 song recorded long before I was even born, but as the bass kicked in and the lyrics filled the room, Sam started to dance. DC shook his head, smiling at the absurdity of it all. 'There's a rat in my kitchen, what am I going to do?' Sam sang. 'I'm going to fix that rat that's what I'm going to do.'

She winked at me mischievously, the cheeky mare.

Oliver is obsessed with reaching big audiences, regardless of whether they listen to Radio 1 or watch the *Ten O'Clock News*. So DC is going to be dragged on to the *This Morning* sofa and forced to drink more cups of tea with the *One Show* presenters. The boss will do whatever it takes, of course, but it's not his favourite part of the job. 'A duty rather than a pleasure,' he told Boy George today. 'And I draw the line at *Loose Women*.'

'If only Ryan Giggs had said the same,' George replied.

Friday 15 April – evening

The evening crept up on me quickly, and before I knew it, it was 6.30 and I was slipping out of the big black door just as the sun was setting above Downing Street.

The street was deserted except for a smattering of film crews and some TV reporters stood in a huddle across the street, wearing coats despite the warm weather and puffing away on fags. The street is narrow as well as long and straight and it acts as a wind tunnel, whipping a light breeze into a stiff wind on all but the calmest of days. Loose pages from a newspaper were being blown down Downing Street, spiralling in the air then falling to the ground.

I squinted in the sunlight, fixing my gaze on the end of the road, where the black railings end and the security gates begin. At first I thought they hadn't turned up, but then I caught a glimpse of King Rat, emerging from nowhere onto the pavement, looking to his right and then to his left, and scrambling towards the rendezvous point. The rest of them were right behind him. I counted them all out from my spot next to the wall and, later on, I counted them all back in again. Then one of them clocked me and nodded in my direction, and the rest of them turned to look. We eyed each other for at least a minute.

'Well, nothing ventured,' I whispered to myself, and starting walking slowly towards them. They stayed completely still, frozen to the spot, they didn't leg it, and in 30 seconds I was sat no less than five yards away from the bunch of young offenders who've been making my life a misery for the last eight weeks.

'I'm Larry,' I said.

King Rat cleared his throat. 'Adam,' he said. 'And this is Gazza, Bobby, Cheryl, Keegan, Ant, Dec and Jackie.' It was Cheryl and Gazza I'd cornered in the attic room a few weeks back.

'You've got half a very good football team here,' I said to King Rat.

'Yeah,' he replied, laughing. 'Or a very bad pop band.'

That seemed to break the ice. A few of them even looked like they might have been laughing, although in my experience rats don't laugh so much as snigger.

King Rat pulled my tail a bit about the mousetraps I'd loaded with Roquefort and Dolcelatte.

'I can't believe you made us eat that foreign muck,' he said. 'Next time how about some good old honest English Cheddar?'

But it was good-natured joshing so I decided to outline my plan quickly while it seemed like we were on good terms.

'Move into the Commons,' I said, cutting to the chase. 'I've cased the joint, I know exactly how to get in – and there's plenty of space.'

King Rat's face fell. 'There's nothing common about us, man.'

I could see I'd pitched this badly, and I began to lose my composure.

'I know, but it's called the House of Commons for historical reasons,' I blurted out.

'And we're not daft either,' he replied, his squeaky

voice growing deeper. 'Besides, have you seen the chamber recently? It's standing room only at PMQs. The place is full enough to bursting, man.'

'Yeah,' Gazza interjected suddenly, and unwelcomely. 'You'd have more chance of finding a seat at St James's Park on a Saturday afternoon.'

The rest of them found this hilarious, and descended into giggles.

'There's always the Lords?' I suggested, without really thinking about what I was saying, but that caused even greater hilarity.

'Do you know how many party donors and flunkies Cameron's ennobled since his lot scraped in?' King Rat asked.

I could tell from his tone that he didn't expect an answer, and besides, I didn't have a clue.

'If all the Lords and Ladies turned up at the same time even two chambers might not be enough to accommodate them,' he said, guffawing.

King Rat turned his back and began to walk away. The rest of them started to follow, with Gazza bringing up the rear.

'Hold up, guys, hold up!' I pleaded.

But it was too late. I'd lost the argument. I slunk back to No 10 in a blacker mood than ever before.

I had all the answers to the difficult questions I expected them to ask at the tips of my claws, and I'd been up half the night rehearsing them. Yes, security is tight, I had planned to say, but I've got mates in security at Downing Street who know precisely when the plods take their tea breaks. (Besides, there have been numerous breaches before. Any clown could pose as a member of Joe Public, blag their way into a select committee hearing and end up sat a few feet away from a minister or a powerful business-man.)

I even had a map drawn out in pencil by Ted, which showed the main underground routes out of Downing Street and the way the network of tunnels hollowed out before the war connect Nos 10 and 11 to other buildings dotted around Whitehall. If ever there was a foolproof plan, this was it.

And I still say it was an inspired idea – one which had been taking shape in my mind ever since DC first told me about the awkward squad he has to contend with down at the old House of Commons. Why not persuade my own awkward squad to decamp to Parliament, where there are more functions every night than they hold at the Élysée Palace, and the rat pack would have the run of the entire Palace of Westminster each summer, when the politicians pack up and go on their long annual break? As far as I'm concerned, I would have been performing the ultimate public service by rounding up all the rats in one place – I even had visions of the Queen pinning an OBE on to my collar. Now I just feel like a soft southerner who's been outwitted by a bunch of sharp Geordies.

Saturday 16 April – morning

I tried to put yesterday's disastrous negotiations behind me this morning by trying to get up to speed on the latest political developments (well, if my time here is drawing to a close I may as well learn as much as I can – it might even come in useful one day).

All this chatter about the coalition confuses me. From where I'm curled up it looks like a Conservative government to me. There's a Conservative Prime Minister, a Conservative Chancellor, a Conservative Home Secretary and . . . well, you get my drift.

Ed Miliband spends most of his time having a pop at Nicky but as far as I can see he's the only one around here with no power at all. I bet DC can't believe his luck.

Young Ed delivered a speech up in Newcastle today, not too far from the rodents' home turf.

I was dead on my paws after spending half the night sitting with Harold and Ted but I headed up to the press room after lunch to listen to what Ed had to say. Believe it or not, I'm starting to take more than a passing interest in all this malarkey.

The longer DC stays here, the more chance I've got of becoming a permanent resident, after all.

Miliband said Nicky is 'locked in the boot of a vehicle which is travelling rapidly in the wrong direction'. 'Maybe so,' I muttered to myself, 'but it's DC who's behind the wheel.'

It's not my place to put Ed right, but there's another by-election test coming up on 6 May, in Leicester, and I always like to see a fair fight.

The last time I witnessed a match-up this one-sided was when Chelsea beat West Brom 6–0 on the first day of last season.

To be fair, Labour should win this one easily, but the tension at this place is unbearable nevertheless.

No one is expecting the Lib Dems to do well, but I reckon it could be Barnsley all over again – and Nicky's looking more miserable than ever.

DC was reading the paper from the comfort of his favourite chair in the White Dining Room this morning, while Clegg stood in the hallway outside.

'At least you can't come sixth this time,' he said.

'I don't see why not,' Nicky said, scuffing the soles of his trainers petulantly against the doorframe.

'Because there are only five candidates,' DC sniggered.

Evening

As Harold was logging off for the night he opened the top drawer to reach for his keys. 'By the way, where's that mobile that was hidden in here got to?' he asked Ted.

'Search me, mate,' Ted shrugged.

I wish they wouldn't be so flippant. I know it's an old handset but it might still have a few state secrets on it given that it belonged to DC.

And those rats are more than capable of sneaking in here and swiping it.

Sunday 17 April

Everyone's talking about clothes.

The papers are reporting that DC won't wear top hat and tails because he'll look 'too posh'.

It's all because of that terrible photo – the Bullingdon Club shot with him and his Oxford mates dressed up like a bunch of monkeys. How much must DC regret posing for that picture? No wonder he keeps his copy locked away in that cupboard in the Terracotta Room upstairs.

Boris Johnson, the king over the water at City Hall, was in that picture too, only he seems to have got away with it. Then again, would anyone let him near Downing Street? Novelty acts never get to the top in politics. Sam Cam was giving DC a hard time in the Den this afternoon when she dropped by on her way out to do a spot of hat shopping.

'But you are posh, David,' she said, when he told her what was going on.

'So are you, Samantha.'

'Yes, but I'm not embarrassed about it.'

'Look, Craig Oliver has already told the press I will be wearing a lounge suit,' DC said.

'Well, if you're going to let Craig Oliver tell you what to wear . . .'

'He doesn't think you should wear a hat either, by the way,' DC said.

Mrs C paused, but she's always got a clever come-back. I often think she should be in the cabinet herself.

'I haven't bought one yet,' she said, 'so that makes things easy.'

'Look, Sam, I'm just glad Olly's made a decision,' DC replied. 'I think it's a trend we should encourage.'

Later that day, it was decided DC would be wearing a morning suit after all. Apparently the paper is now being told the lounge suit line was 'misbriefed'.

I never met Andy Coulson, but I'm fairly sure he'd be using some pretty choice language if he was still around.

To be honest, I've been reaching for a profanity or two myself of late, given my failure to round up those rodents, and when I started checking those rat traps again this evening I did so with a heavy heart.

I'd left some loaded up with Cheddar in the basement, though I was under no illusions about the chances of success. But setting and checking the traps has become a sort of ritual, a way of filling my time.

All the cheese had disappeared, as always, replaced by a note, so I braced myself for another sardonic missive ribbing me about my general uselesness. In fact, King Rat had penned a polite invitation to a second summit: 'We kindly request the company of Larry the cat at a forum to discuss future living arrangements' it read. The suggested venue was the same as before – on the pavement outside No 10 – and the day, Wednesday, was sooner than I could have hoped for. 'Failure to respond to this notice will be regarded as confirmation that you plan to attend' the invite ended.

They are cheeky buggers, those rodents, but I'll show up on Wednesday. To be fair I don't think I really have much choice. And in any case, I have a proposal of my own to put to them.

Monday 18 April – morning

There are three days each year when my spirits soar: the first day of the new football season, Christmas Day (even down at Battersea we used to get a present or two) and a day like today – the first warm, sunny spring day of the year.

I went out back to smokers' corner in the late afternoon, just to feel the sun's glow on my fur and before long I was stretched out on the warm pavement, purring ostentatiously. It was then that I was reminded that all sorts of nonsense goes on around the back of No 10. As I was luxuriating on the floor, catching some rays, I spotted a shady-looking character in a shabby suit handing over a bunch of readies to a fat-necked bloke in a smart suit who's been on 'street security'. Once the transaction was over, the shabby-suit nearly tripped over me in his rush to exit the scene. I let out a loud hiss and he came to a sudden stop, stumbled, and dropped the bag to the floor. A phone fell out.

The shabby stranger looked flustered. He grabbed it from the pavement, where it had landed with a clutter right next to my head, before legging it to his car. That's when I clocked the badge pinned to his lapel, the word 'Press' written on it in big black letters.

Afternoon

The new Irish Prime Minister was in this afternoon, and the geezer who runs Poland dropped in for lunch. One of the staff had to leg it to the *Polski sklep* down in Pimlico to make sure we had enough sausages in. It's surprising how quickly a cat can become blasé about meeting all these world leaders. Frankly, my old china, if they're not in the G8, I'm not really interested.

They all have to go through security, whoever they are – sheikhs, kings, presidents or film stars. Even

141

Kate Moss had to bring her passport when she turned up for Sam Cam's fashion bash the other month.

In fact, I'm about the only one who can skip right through the checkpoints without being stopped and searched, which still gives me a thrill if I stop and think about it.

Once the dignitaries and all their staff have been given the once-over, they're deposited in a pokey little holding room to the left of the big black door, which isn't that much bigger than the cage I was locked up in down in Battersea.

I've seen dictators squeezed in there, leafing through copies of *The Economist*, as if they're waiting to be called through to see the doctor. Sometimes their entourages sit idly on the sofa in the hallway outside, opposite a cabinet full of colonial trinkets from the days of Empire. There are a few ceremonial cutlasses and sabres fixed to the wall, too, which makes me wonder why they bother with all those security checks. What's the point of confiscating loaded weapons, then letting bodyguards loose in a corridor full of swords?

Tuesday 19 April

DC was up at dawn this morning to go on the *Today* programme. He told Evan Davis he didn't think

Gordon Brown should be the next head of something called the IMF.

George was in No 10 at the time listening to the radio.

'Never mind the IMF,' he said. 'He shouldn't even be allowed to run MFI.'

All the teenage helpers laughed too loudly. You can always tell who is on the up in this place by the reception their bad jokes get.

DC wasn't pulling any punches on the wireless this morning.

'Just look at the mess he left behind!' he said, or words to that effect. I don't know why Gordon couldn't clean up after himself like I always do, but DC seems determined to ruin what's left of his predecessor's career. Sometimes I think the PM has got a vindictive streak as wide as Whitehall.

The boss did try to show his softer side later on, hanging around the BBC studios to deliver some racing tips to listeners.

The sports presenter warned DC it would be the last time he'd be allowed to do it if his horses didn't perform, so I insisted on turning Sky over to the Channel 4 racing coverage this afternoon to see if his tips came in.

'Red Samantha' finished ninth out of eleven and the boss's other tip, 'Stormin' Gordon', finished seventh.

'You're fired!' I told DC, when the last race was run. I've always wanted to say that.

One of the papers counted the number of words the presenter with the nipple ring came out with during his chat with DC this morning. He managed 7,000 and the PM got through 11,000 – even though he was the one answering the questions. Proof at last that hacks really do love the sound of their own voices.

Wednesday 20 April

There were no pleasantries at our second summit this morning when we gathered on the sun-kissed Downing Street pavement along the way from No 10, just a prolonged silence which turned into a tense stand-off. The hot weather we've had all month has been great, but No 10 is an old building with old-fashioned ventilation and stuffy low-ceilinged rooms, and a lot of us who live there have been overheating of late.

So King Rat was in no mood for a chat as his acolytes stood shiftily behind him in a line, grim-faced, preferring instead to make me an offer he hoped I'd accept.

'The truth is we feel a bit sorry for you, like,' he said.

I thought King Rat was pulling my proverbial, so I

sat myself down on the warm concrete floor and prepared myself for another tongue-lashing from the
gobby north-east awkward squad.

But he insisted he wanted to end our game of cat
and mouse once and for all, or at least negotiate a truce.

'Look, Lazzer,' he said. 'We want to make a deal.
You stop trying to catch us, and we'll stop showing
you up, like.'

As long as they were free to run around the place,
he said, they'd stop rubbing my noses in it by nobbling
TV interviews and turning up uninvited at No 10
receptions.

My heart sank. They just don't get it, these rodents.
Every time they appear on people's TV screens, scut-
tling up and down Downing Street in full view of the
cameras, my rep is shredded. My pride can't handle
being the first chief rat-catcher to get turfed out before
I've even served a full term in office.

So I counted to ten, thanked them politely for their
proposal, and then hit them with my final offer.

'Listen lads,' I said, 'I'd love to get all Stevie
Wonder on you and tell you we can live together in
perfect harmony, but the truth is this place just isn't
big enough for all of us.'

The rats shook their heads in unison and started
muttering to one another, but I pressed on regardless,
just like DC does when he's trying to make a point at
PMQs and he raises his voice above the din coming
from the green benches opposite.

'You say the Commons isn't good enough and only No 10 will do,' I told them, 'but there's a better place down the road. I'm talking about the most exclusive piece of real estate in the world.'

King Rat looked curious. 'Go on, man. We're all ears, like.'

That's true, I thought, but I kept it to myself and concentrated on my sales pitch.

'Buckingham Palace!' I said. 'Ancestral home to the nation's rulers for centuries. The gardens alone are twenty times the size of No 10.'

A stunned silence descended on Downing Street, and my proposal hung in the air longer than a bad joke at an after-dinner speech. But then King Rat shot it down, just as I thought he might.

'Sorry, Laz,' King Rat said. 'You're a canny cat, but we know our place. There's no way we can live in a palace.'

I knew they'd have trouble getting their pointy little heads around the idea of sharing a mansion with a bunch of blue-blooded types, so I cleared my throat and embarked on my next speech, closing my eyes and imagining for a moment that I was at the despatch box before a crucial Commons vote.

'Listen,' I began. 'They're no posher than this lot at No 10. Kate Middleton even went to the same school as Sam.'

They listened as I told them that if Sam was ten years younger she might be the one getting married in a few days' time. 'Princess Samantha,' I said. 'It's got a certain ring to it.'

I told them Wills and Harry were at Eton a few years after Cameron. They had no idea. I told them that Mrs C's ancestors were the original owners of Buckingham Palace.

I carried on firing out the facts I'd filleted from the copy of Debrett's in DC's en suite toilet like bullets from a machine gun.

'Sam's bloodline can be traced back to King Charles II,' I told them. 'DC is descended from George II.'

'They're both true blues,' I said. 'They're even posher than the Buckingham Palace lot.'

Even my worst enemies would concede I've got the gift of the gab, but King Rat still looked unconvinced, so I played my final card.

'Listen lads,' I said, 'and ladette' (I nodded at Cheryl). 'I know what you're thinking. You don't really belong in either place – none of us do.'

The rats stared at the pavement.

'But you won't be moving in to the Queen's gaff – you'll be liberating it! Just imagine – they'll have to rename it "The People's Palace"!'

The rodents seemed to lighten up a bit and huddled together conspiratorially.

Finally, they broke up again and turned to face me in a line.

'Alreet,' King Rat said. 'We'll think about it. But this isn't a "yes", mind.'

'At last,' I thought, as I trotted back to No 10. 'A breakthrough.'

To be honest, I was puffed up with pride that I delivered my speech word for word, just as I'd rehearsed it. It was positively Churchillian, even if I do say so myself.

Thursday 21 April – morning

All this talk about the wedding reminds me of my old granddad. He was a bit of a rabble rouser, always banging on about the common cat getting his share, but he was a sentimental old git deep down and I know he shed a tear when Di and Charles got hitched.

Granddad used to talk about the street parties everyone threw back in '81 and now we're all set for a replay.

Mr C has put in a request to hold her own bash in Downing Street, which I reckon is one request that should be waved through by Westminster Council. Well, they can't turn down the PM's wife, can they? Then again, she's had a few minor disagreements with the burghers down on Victoria Street over the work she oversaw at the No 11 flat.

They wanted to move a doorway but the council got all uppity about it because No 10's a listed building. It was supposed to be a minor facelift but it ended up as reconstructive surgery, as far as I can tell, although DC paid for most of it out of his own pocket.

I can't help wondering if us lot had to fork out for the rest of it though, which doesn't seem particularly fair given the tough times we've been having. It's not like DC's short of a few bob, is it?

Mind you, he's no fool — the boss knows a good party is just what the country needs.

Boy George is walking around the place with a long face, which must mean the economy's stalling again, libraries are closing and council workers are being laid off. But stories about the big day are knocking all that gloomy stuff down the news agenda. Another four-day weekend can't fail to make us feel a bit more chipper either. Anyone who's not a fan of the Windsors can always cheer on the Middletons instead.

Kate was out on the King's Road down Chelsea way again today, popping into Jigsaw, Whistles and Banana Republic. I doubt the snappers will ever get a shot of her carrying a Matalan bag, but at least she's not shopping at Harvey Nicks. The PR people at the Palace are smart enough to realize that wouldn't look too clever when the unemployment lines are getting bigger.

It does make me chuckle when posh people find something they like on the high street — it's as if they've stumbled across something wearable at the school jumble sale. Besides, I know the King's Road well and it's definitely not your average high street — there's no Argos, for a start.

The punters are lapping it up regardless. Virtually every paper had a picture of Ms Middleton out shopping with her mates on their front page this morning – even the serious ones which nobody reads.

As for the tabloids – well, Kate's their new darling, but if she's not careful she'll also be attracting more attention from the paparazzi than anyone should have to put up with, the poor luv. She's that popular she could even knock Lady Gaga off the front pages of the red tops right now.

But like I said, Kate's advisors at the Palace have got the right idea, making sure she's seen in the sort of shops most of us could afford to splash out in once in a while (at a stretch). She'll be photographed popping into Nando's for her tea before you know it, or throwing a birthday bash in Frankie & Benny's.

I like to picture Kate and Wills sitting in their new digs in north Wales once they've moved in after the wedding, surrounded by cardboard boxes with IKEA stamped on the front and wooden crates full of new kitchenware from BHS.

I think Sam Cam might have to tone down the designer gear as long as Kate's on the scene, especially while this downturn is dragging on endlessly.

Then again I'm sure I overheard Craig Oliver trying to persuade her to shop at H&M the other day.

'Listen,' Sam told him. 'I wore that M&S dress, and that's as far as I'm willing to go.'

Don't get me wrong, I'm no republican but personally

I still think all this 'everywoman' stuff is part of the act the royals put on to make sure us commoners don't think they are too high and mighty. It's fine by me, because they're grafters when all is said and done. They might even set an example to some of the loafers in Blighty who get something in exchange for doing bugger all.

Thursday 21 April – afternoon

King Rat's answer came, just as I thought it might, written on a note – a tattered old piece of Downing Street headed paper which had been gnawed through in one of the corners – and left in one of the rat traps that proved to be so bloody ineffectual. At least they finally came in useful for something today.

I retrieved it carefully from one of the traps in the pillared room and took it back to my basket to open it out of sight, alone on my Wills and Kate cushion. I swear my paws were shaking as I unfolded it.

It was as if I was checking a winning lottery ticket or opening a letter telling me whether I'd landed my dream job (centre-forward for Chelsea FC, in case you were wondering).

I opened it up carefully with my eyes closed and then slowly opened them again. The message gradually came into focus.

'Aye, g'wan then,' it read. It was a yes.

Never have three little words meant so much to me – or at least not since I fell for Kitty, the beautiful Persian I had a fling with all those years ago, and she whispered to me that my feelings were reciprocated.

I leaned back on my cushion, relief coursing through my fur, and purred louder than I have ever purred in my life.

'It's Buckingham Palace or bust,' I said to myself, and drifted off into a long and blissful sleep.

Friday 22 April – morning

There's something I never expected to see in the *Sun* today: a picture of a topless Rebekah Brooks! Don't worry. I'm just pulling your proverbial. But until today, I would have said there was more chance of seeing Rebekah on Page 3 than there was of opening the paper and spotting Ed Miliband staring back at me, pool cue in hand and a slightly lopsided grin spread across his boat race.

The *Sun* has run a soft-focus interview with Ed that *OK!* magazine would have turned down as too one-sided. Even the headline would have gone down well at Labour HQ, I reckon: 'Red Ed is dead' it said – and that from the paper that lumbered him with the nickname to start with.

I was still reading the article when DC strolled into

the press room and pulled the paper from under me. It's the first time I've ever seen the boss lose it.

'After everything I've done for them!' he shouted, turning as red as the *Sun*'s masthead.

'All those stories we gave them on a plate. The exclusive interviews, the visits to Wapping. I even had to have dinner with Rebekah and that husband of hers in Oxfordshire on Boxing Day!'

He was straight on the phone to Rebekah after that, demanding to know what had happened, although it took a little time to track her down.

It's Easter, after all, and she was up in the country with her other half, Charlie, in the rural retreat they own down the road from Dave and Sam's constituency home.

By the time he got through to Brooks on her mobile he'd calmed down a bit, and Rebekah soon talked him down from the ceiling with her soothing tone.

'Listen, we have to at least pretend to be fair,' she said, laughing. 'And besides, haven't you noticed the date?'

'Good Friday?'

'Exactly,' Rebekah said. 'The one day when nobody buys a bloody paper!'

There's a tight little social circle down there in the Chilterns. They call it 'the Chipping Norton set'. Gramps' daughter Elisabeth has a place in the hills with her PR husband Matthew, and that bloke off *Top Gear* Jeremy Clarkson is always popping in for a drink or ten. I'd say more decisions get made in Oxfordshire than they do at No 10, and I'm not talking about what they're going to stick in the AGA for lunch.

Friday 22 April – afternoon

It was a day of reckoning for me. A day when, if everything went smoothly, I knew I'd probably end up extending my stay at No 10. Now I know how DC will feel when he goes to the country in four years' time.

The boss tricked Nicky into forming a coalition so he could get into Downing Street, but I've gone one better by persuading those rats to help me out of a tight spot. I told them we had to prove we can work together before I bust them out of here next month.

DC was still grouchy after lunch. I think he was worried about the *Sun*'s Miliband piece, despite Rebekah's assurances, so when I jumped through the window in the room where the garden girls work, rat in mouth, everyone in the place was relieved I'd lightened the mood.

Cheryl put on a great performance, twitching and shaking and generally making out like she was in agony, before rolling around on the floor and, finally, expiring with a squeak.

The garden girls all rushed around to stroke me – even the boss himself – and that's when Cheryl made a dash for it, disappearing through the same window I'd climbed through minutes earlier.

Everyone was so caught up in the moment they didn't even notice she'd done a runner, and even if they had I'm not convinced they would have cared. As far as they were concerned, I'd finally justified DC's faith in me and proved he'd been right to hire me. I wasn't just another gimmick or a PR stunt.

It hardly mattered whether the little blighter was dead or alive.

Sam jumped in the lift and raced up to the flat, returning with some Harvey Nicks caviar from her new SMEG fridge, and spooned it into my bowl. I can't stand the stuff myself, but I swallowed it out of courtesy.

'Well, we haven't had that much to celebrate recently,' Sam said, when she caught DC looking over at her disapprovingly.

After all the fuss was over and everyone had got back to work, I glanced out of that window and into the garden outside. Sure enough, the rats were out there, just as we'd agreed, giving me thumbs-up signs. King Rat winked at me from his hiding place behind the blue delphiniums Sam planted last year when she ripped out those red roses.

I've got a new bowl now with the stars and stripes painted on one side and the Union Jack on the other, to mark the Dude's visit to Blighty next month with his wife Michelle. I reckon President Obama will make Kate and Wills look like a warm-up act, but he's probably the only man on the planet who could follow a royal wedding. Well, he is political royalty, after all.

Saturday 23 April

There's a row brewing at this place over the way 'sharp-elbowed' middle-class people manage to wangle work experience for their kids at prestigious places like No 10.

My old man used to call it giving someone a leg up, helping them clamber on to the bottom rung of life's ladder, if you like. Nicky Clegg is making a right song and dance about the fact that interns don't get paid because he reckons only rich people can afford to go without a wage, even at that age.*

Maybe he's on to something – I haven't come across too many people from the wrong side of the tracks at

---

* I wonder if that makes me an 'intern'? I get fed and watered and there's a roof over my head, but there's no pay packet at the end of the week. I may have to have a word with young Nicky.

this place, only the rats and me, although I suppose Harriet's a bit of a rough diamond.

If nothing else, we could certainly do with someone who knows how to make a good cuppa around here, because I've downed enough of Sam's peppermint tea to fill a swimming pool and I'm not sure it's doing much for my digestive system.

I left a nasty deposit on Sam Cam's Smythson calf-skin iPad case the other day and she hasn't spoken to me since.

I could hear Nicky and the boss having a ding-dong in the Den from my basket on the floor below.

'How "sharp-elbowed" was your father?' DC asked.

'I've no idea what you're talking about.'

'Only I have it on good authority that he helped you land a job at a Finnish bank, Nicky Boy.'

'Er . . . yes, that's true.'

It turns out Nicky had THREE unpaid placements before he got around to landing a proper job.

It's hardly surprising the boss isn't singing from the same social mobility hymn sheet when it comes to internships. After all, how do you think he got his first break? Some family friend who also happened to be a minor member of the aristocracy belled No 10 on the morning he turned up for a job interview to tell them they were about to meet 'an exceptional young man'. And the rest, as they say, is history.

DC gave an interview to the *Daily Telegraph* today

and said he wouldn't be budging on the intern issue.

'Actually I've got my neighbour coming in for an internship in a few weeks,' he told them.

'That's not a very nice way to talk about Boy George,' I told him when I passed him on the stairs this evening.

Sunday 24 April

The invitations have started to arrive.

I can tell you that the only surprise, now that I'm someone who can tell his 'big beasts' from his political pygmies, is that Jeremy Hunt made the cut.

If Gramps was in with the Royals I'd say Hunt had been handed a reward for his part in OK-ing his big deal to buy Sky TV the other month.

I know Hunt was angling for an invite and Gramps pulls some pretty big strings from his little room up there in the attic.

Only he hates the monarchy almost as much as he hates the BBC and he'd sooner go to the TUC annual conference than turn up at Kate and Wills' bash.

To be honest, I don't know why he's quite so mean-spirited about the whole affair. He won't be complaining when a few hundred thousand more people buy the *Sun* every day this week, after all – all those 60ps add up to a fair bit of wonga.

The other guests include Ed Miliband (I reckon he'll have to hire top hat and tails), but Blair and Brown aren't invited, even though Thatcher and Major have been, and there are plenty of people getting upset on Tony and Gordon's behalf.

I don't know why all these reds are so angry about missing out on one of the most elitist events in human history. Mandy is making a right fuss about not going. Anyone would think he was minor royalty himself. Well, I suppose they do call him the Prince of Darkness. Still, he'll probably get an invite to some billionaire's birthday party on a luxury yacht later down the line, so what does he care?

DC and Mrs C are in Cornwall for a few days. They were trying to make it a low-key affair, but there are pictures of the family all over the papers. There's no chance of getting a moment's peace these days now that everyone's got one of those camera phones. The problem for DC is he can't really complain about it — not when he has to keep all those editors sweet.

Monday 25 April

At the very end of the corridor, at the western end of Downing Street, past the ceremonial swords and the room where the foreign visitors sit flicking idly through copies of *The Economist*, past the join in the carpet which marks the border between No 10 and No 11, and behind the door of No 12, there's a horseshoe-shaped room flanked by two offices.

This is where old Gordon Brown had his bunker in his final days, hunkered down like a cornered rodent after the country had a bit of a wobble last May, when it decided to kick him out of No 10 but couldn't quite bring itself to hand the keys to DC.

It wasn't until young Nicky Clegg got involved that the mess was sorted out.

A little further back, there's another suite of oak-panelled rooms with big sash windows which were used as Gordy's dressing room – the place where his staff hung his shirts. The odd metal coat-hanger still gets found behind a desk every now and then.

No 12 is used by the government whips who keep Tory and Lib Dem MPs in line, just as it was before Gordon commandeered it, so imagine my surprise when I bumped into Boy George in one of the quieter offices, talking into his mobile phone.

I'd only gone down there myself to have a bit of a preen in private – I don't like to cough up fur-balls in front of the staff – but George looked even more surprised to see me than I was to see him.

'Just get as many tickets as you can,' he whispered into his phone, and placed it back in the pocket of his dark blue suit.

'It's the only place you can get a bloody reception*
in this place,' he explained, looking sheepish.

'You don't have to answer to me,' I replied.

Tuesday 26 April

Sam and Dave were complaining about spending
another weekend break surrounded by snappers. It
can't be much fun.

'The strange thing is they were all waiting for us at
that ice-cream van,' DC mused, this morning, 'but you
hadn't told anyone we were going there – not even me.'

'I did leave a message on your phone asking you to
meet me and the kids there,' Sam said. 'That's why I
thought it was strange when you turned up at the
hotel instead.'

DC frowned. 'You didn't use my old phone, did
you? I haven't used that one since we last went to
Chequers,' he said, shaking his head. 'Get with the
programme, Sam.'

Mrs C just looked bemused.

That's when the penny dropped, although I still
don't think those two are any the wiser.

---

* He's right. There are some parts of Downing Street where it's almost
impossible to use a mobile phone. Still, it's not as if anyone would need to call
the Prime Minister's office in an emergency.

The security boys don't like the boss to use the same phone for very long, in case it ends up in the wrong hands. The trouble is that I think this one might have done – courtesy of King Rat and the shady company he keeps.

Mrs C spent the day cooking cupcakes in the Downing Street kitchen for the royal wedding street party she's hosting on Friday. When I heard she had four little helpers with her, I thought those bloody rats had reneged on our deal, but they turned out to be kids from one of the charities she supports. The cakes were decorated with edible pictures of Kate and Wills on top. I know a few people who wouldn't mind having a nibble on Ms Middleton before she goes up the aisle, but I better not be disrespectful to a future queen – I might get locked up in the Tower or, worse still, get sent back to SW11.

DC was busy entertaining the Prime Minister of New Zealand, although hardly anyone recognized the unfamiliar bloke who was wandering around No 10.

'Who's that?' Boy George asked me at one point.

'It's the Prime Minister of New Zealand,' I said. 'Who did you think it was, the bloke who's come round to fix the boiler?'

'Don't be absurd,' he replied. 'I thought he was my new driver.'

Boy George gestured at the peaked cap he was holding in his right hand.

'I was about to hand him this,' he said.

Now that really would have been the icing on the cake.

Ed Miliband is having his adenoids out, but the papers keep writing that he's having a 'nose job'. DC said today he hoped he wouldn't have a charisma implant while he's on the operating table. 'I don't think they do those on the NHS,' I said. Poor Ed. But there'll always be a job for him at Aardman Animations as the next *Creature Comforts* character if the politics lark doesn't work out.

Wednesday 27 April

DC got into a spot of bother at PMQs today when he told some Labour Doris called Angela Eagle to stop flapping around.

'Calm down, dear,' he told her, in that voice Michael Winner uses on the TV ads. She didn't like that at all.

When he arrived back, a portrait of Gordon Brown had appeared above the spiral staircase alongside all the other pictures of prime ministers past. If the language DC uses when he talks about him is anything to go by, it sounds like he'd prefer to have his head delivered to Downing Street on a plate, but he had some fun with Boy George when he spotted it.

'At last!' DC said. 'Gordon Brown is hanging from a nail over the No 10 stairwell!'

In the photograph, Brown had his arms crossed in front of him so they lay over his crotch in what I thought looked a rather uncomfortable pose.

'I see he's still clutching his Balls for comfort!' Osborne said.

'Is that a smile or a grimace, Gordon?' DC said.

I happened to be walking past at the time on my way down to the canteen.

'Calm down, dears,' I told them.

Thursday 28 April

The Australian Prime Minister Julia Gillard was in today. Perhaps she'd heard the guy from New Zealand had been granted an audience with DC and wanted to get in on the act: those Antipodeans can be very competitive, after all. Gillard was born in Wales, emigrated to Oz with her parents when she was a nipper, and now she's running the country. Mrs C thought it made for a lovely tale.

'Her parents were from a town called Barry,' DC said.

'It would have been a better story if it had been called Bruce,' I said.

If I didn't know better, I would have said DC was smirking when he delivered the first few lines of his press conference speech. Gillard didn't look particularly amused.

I suspect all these foreigners are in town for the royal wedding.

The excitement has been building all week, and I noticed this morning that the streets around Parliament have been decked out with lines of Union Jacks, which sway gently in the breeze.

I wouldn't want to try and book a room in any of the hotels on Park Lane at the moment, not that I could afford to. Half of them will be full of aristocrats from Europe and beyond, and the other half will be teeming with scribblers and snappers who have flown in from all over the world, boozing and gossiping. I don't often feel sorry for toffs but I wouldn't wish that on anyone.

The preparations are in full swing now. DC was woken up in the middle of the night by the sound of the soldiers going through their dress rehearsals, which started before dawn, and he wasn't in the best of moods this evening. You can always tell when a big state occasion is going on in the capital because horse manure starts to appear on the tarmac. When I walked out on to Whitehall this afternoon to get a bit of fresh air there were piles of the stuff.

To be brutally honest, it reminded me of what comes out of the Palace's PR department. They announced today that two of Wills and Kate's bridesmaids and page-boys are called Grace Van Cutsem and Billy Lowther-Pinkerton. 'People's Wedding' my whiskers!

Friday 29 April – morning

She looked beautiful. Of course she did. And Pippa was a sight to behold as well – particularly from behind.

It was cloudy over Westminster Abbey, and slightly chilly too, but this is England, after all, and at least it didn't rain on Kate's gloriously understated dress.

Like I said before, my old granddad was a sentimental old cat, and I reckon I'm more like him than I sometimes care to admit. After they'd exchanged vows and swapped rings, and after Harry had whispered something naughty into Will's ear as Kate walked slowly up that aisle, after 'Jerusalem' started up and I'd taken my place, unofficial like, at the back of the pews, I felt something rousing in my chest.

And the only word I can think of to describe it is 'patriotism', not a word that's often used these days. I'm not ashamed to tell you all I shed a tear or two right there, sat as I was underneath a pew, well out of sight of all those pompous types. I couldn't see what was going on but I could hear it alright, and I could feel it too. Call me soft, but despite all our problems, there's nothing like a wedding to remind everyone that, for most of us, life isn't all that bad.

Later on, they appeared on the balcony and sealed the day with a kiss, and after stepping inside for a drink or three with the new in-laws, they added a traditional twist, driving out of the Palace in William's convertible Aston Martin, tin cans tied to the boot.

I thought that was a nice touch.

I was proud to be a Londoner today, and proud to be British. I know it doesn't really make much sense, but I'm going to seize the moment before it evaporates and enjoy it before things get back to normal.

The fact is most people were happier today than they were yesterday and happier than they'll be tomorrow. That's something worth celebrating in itself, innit? I just hope that with all this fandango going on they don't forget to feed me.

Friday 29 April – afternoon

They stuck a sparkly Union Jack bow-tie around my neck at lunchtime and invited a few snappers in to take shots of me sat on the Cabinet table. I was not amused.

Don't get me wrong. I'm game for a laugh and all that, but I've got a serious job to do here and I'm not too happy about becoming a figure of fun. I can see how the celebrity game could play with your head. It's fine as long as you're famous for the right reasons, but it can be embarrassing if you're not.

The bow-tie was twice the size of my head and I spent the rest of the day clawing at it in a desperate attempt to cut through the elastic. Harriet could see I wasn't enjoying all the attention but after her third glass of Pimm's and lemonade she was too far gone to help, tottering all over the shop on her four-inch heels. Downing Street threw a street party, like so many other places across the country, and I tried to enter into the spirit of things, despite the garish neck-wear.

It kicked off at 2.30, when DC and Mrs C were on the way back from the Palace, so the boss's favourite peer, Baroness Warsi, hosted the bash until they got back, looking fetching in a Union Jack sari.

Hilton's been banging on about using the wedding to try and make us all feel better about the state we're in, or some such nonsense, and he wants ministers to wrap themselves up in the flag. Perhaps Warsi was taking him a bit too literally.

There were nearly 100 guests at the bash, nearly all of them from charities like Save the Children, which Sam Cam does some work for, as well as some kids from local schools. Downing Street was done out a treat.

There was bunting, a brass band and an ice-cream stall, where I managed to blag a 99 from the man who was serving: I'm pretty sure he'd had a few too many sherbets.

The food was made by No 10 staff – Clegg's bird Miriam does a pretty good paella – and the kids seemed to enjoy the children's entertainers while the adults watched the action on a big TV. With the sun shining and everyone gathered around a screen, it was a bit like seeing England play in the World Cup, except everyone knew this time there'd be a happy ending for once.

Saturday 30 April

They are clearing up the debris this morning, sweeping up the plastic flags and picking up the Kate and Wills masks in Hyde Park. The Union Jacks have been taken down from the lampposts and the temporary TV studios lining The Mall have been dismantled.

I assume Kate and Wills will be back at the apartment they share with Harry at Clarence House, at least until after the honeymoon is over and they move into Kensington Palace. Poor old Kate – imagine dossing down with one of your in-laws when you've just tied the knot. They won't be there much, mind you. Rather like some of those celebrity types, they will be living in more than one place for a while, only unlike Hollywood actors who divide their time between LA and New York, Kate and Wills will be splitting their lives between London and Anglesey. It doesn't sound particularly glam does it? But HRH is still a Search and Rescue pilot, of course, so the happy couple will be at their main home in Angelsey most often and their royal residence in London every now and then. Still, two homes is two homes and it seems unlikely they will be slumming it.

I was desperate to find DC to hear all about what he got up to on the big day but he was playing tennis with Boris this morning at Chequers. No, not that Boris; Boris Becker – the youngest ever Wimbledon winner (and the only one to be barred from every restaurant broom cupboard).

I had to wait until the PM got back to London to hear all the gossip.

DC was unusually discreet, telling me how the Speaker's other half, Sally Bercow, who towered over her husband, had a plunging neckline on her dark dress that he very much doubted would have met with royal approval. He reckons Sam overheard Ed Miliband, who looked dapper in his Moss Bros get-up, complaining that he didn't get any decent cut-away shots on television, although unless he was sneaking off to the Abbey toilets to watch ITV on his iPhone I'm not sure how he'd have known. Mrs C would probably get a bit of grief, the boss said, for not wearing a hat, but most of the fashion journalists were saving their most pointed remarks for Beatrice and Eugenie's OTT Philip Treacy hats, and for

Clegg's *señorita* Miriam, who looked like she'd come as a flamenco dancer.

'I tell you what though, Larry,' he said. 'It's good for the country. The best possible advert for UK plc.'

'It's what we do best, sir. The pomp and the pageantry. The tourists'll be flocking back.'

'Too true, Larry,' he said, 'and Mattel are going to do a roaring trade in Pippa Middleton dolls.'

'By the look of the latest growth figures, I'd say we could do with a bit of help,' I said. DC did not look amused.

'Caught any rats today?' he said. 'No? I didn't think so.'

MAY 2011

Sunday 1 May

I was right about Prince Charles. He does have a mischievous streak. There were never going to be piles of invitations for DC and his mates, no matter how many favours the PM did for His Highness. All the top brass were invited – Osborne, Hague and the Home Secretary with the killer heels, Theresa May. But the rest of the 650 or so MPs were whistling in the wind if they thought they were going to get a look in.

I watched the highlights on iPlayer again today – I thought the bloke the BBC got in to direct the whole affair, the one who usually does *The X Factor*, did a bloody good job.

I didn't spot it yesterday, but I saw on the coverage that Jeremy Hunt, the Culture Minister with the tongue-twister name, took his place at the Abbey, which makes me wonder if he could be next in line to DC's throne.

His department helped to organize the bash, along with the Palace, which might explain why he made the cut, but I reckon DC has got bigger plans for him. Well, he is an old Etonian, after all.

As for Charles, he had enough of his own mates to look after without worrying about DC's social circle. There was the marketing man from Audi, for a start, which supplies half the Royal Family with cars. The last two prime ministers must have been slightly miffed they were behind a car rep in the queue for royal invitations, but DC seems convinced the Palace wanted revenge for some of the things the last government got up to.

'Don't forget Charles mentioned he'd fallen out with Blair over fox-hunting,' he told me this afternoon when I ran into him in the garden.

He was taking down the red, white and blue bunting, standing on a small set of ladders and stretching to remove it from the hedges while I followed him around in the sunshine.

'I thought New Labour were OK with the monarchy,' I said. 'Wasn't it Blair who described Diana as the "people's princess"?'

'Yes, as a matter of fact they got the Royal Family out of a bit of a hole,' DC said. 'They persuaded the Queen to come over all touchy feely, and it might even have saved their bacon. The problem was they never stopped boasting about it.'

'Bad manners,' I said. DC nodded. 'But what about Brown?' I said. 'What did he do?'

'Oh, they think he persuaded Blair to decommission the royal yacht Britannia,' DC said. 'Painful one that. The Queen looked devastated when it sailed for the last time. I believe it's the only time she's ever shed a tear in public.' DC rolled up a Union Flag and tossed it non-chalantly into a bin-liner with Steve Hilton's name on it.

Monday 2 May

Osama Bin Laden – the world's public enemy No 1 – is dead. It's good news, of course, but how stupid do I look in comparison? The Americans have tracked down and caught the world's most wanted man, and I've only managed to take out a single lousy rat – and even that was a fit-up.

Fair play to the boys from the US – they found their target and dispatched Osama with cool efficiency – but if I'm being totally straight with you, my heart sank when I heard the news. I was watching *Daybreak* when I found out; only the presenters were so excited about the aftermath of the royal wedding they didn't get around to mentioning it for at least fifteen minutes.

Here I am, sitting in the heart of government, and I must have been one of the last in the country to hear. What a numpty.

Tuesday 3 May – morning

The Cabinet Room looks spectacular when the sun is shining. The light floods in through windows that seem ten-foot tall, at least to a little fella like me. I like to stretch out on one of the window-sills on Tuesday mornings, after we've finished breakfast with the family and we've had our morning chat in the bathroom. That way I'm still there when DC chairs the first of his two big weekly meetings.

The cabinet all file in mid-morning and take their places at the oval-shaped table, shuffling their papers and smiling insincerely at each other.

Away from the table, on chairs set out by the double doors, which lead directly on to DC's study, Olly and Gabby sit in silence with his other advisors.

Then the doors are flung open dramatically and DC strides in.

It's quite an impressive performance. And it's the only time I really see Dave as the Prime Minister rather than the bloke I chat to every morning while he's shaving in the bathroom mirror.

Tuesday 3 May – afternoon

There was drama in Cabinet today. I trotted out of the room after a few minutes when they started talking about AV, escaping through the big doors that open out on to the garden and curling up on the sun-kissed terrace.

But DC told me afterwards that Chris Huhne, one of

the Lib Dem lot, had started making a song and dance about the AV vote, waving around some leaflets the 'No' campaign have been stuffing through letterboxes. He wanted DC and Boy George to apologize for 'getting personal' and telling lies, which is a bit rich when you consider the number of promises the Lib Dems have broken since they became part of the government.

Eventually the Chancellor snapped. 'This is the Cabinet, not some sub-Jeremy Paxman interview,' he said.

A couple of hours later the media knew all about what had happened at Cabinet. I wonder how they found out.

No one makes a fool of DC and I reckon he and Boy George are already thinking about how best to put that little upstart Huhne in his place once and for all.

'The thing is, Larry, Nicky knows his place,' he said, 'and so does the ginger rodent.' (I think he was talking about Danny Alexander, the servant who kept filling up George's glass on Budget day.) 'But Huhne has ideas above his station.'

The next thing you know, Nicky burst in, in floods of tears, crying that Huhne wants his job.

I have to say I was pretty impressed with DC's parenting skills.

'There, there, Nicky,' he said, mopping the tears from his eyes with a red, white and blue Kleenex left over from the royal wedding street party he found in the top drawer of his desk.

'Don't you worry, we'll take care of Huhne,' he said. 'I promise.'

He leaned back in his chair, cracked his knuckles and picked up the phone.

'See what dirt you can dig up on that rat Chris Huhne,' he said, replacing the receiver. 'And let's keep this conversation between the two of us.'

'Or the three of us,' I said from my place in the corner. I think this is one promise to Nicky that DC might even keep. Like I said on my second day on the job, politics is a tough old game. Dog eat dog, in fact. Makes me glad I'm a feline.

DC arrived back from BBC Television Centre early this morning looking like the cat who'd got the proverbial cream. I've never seen him so full of himself. He'd been on the *Today* programme to talk about AV, a debate that must have had all those stock-brokers in Surrey yawning over their jam on toast. Humphrys hasn't got his head around the new system and DC took him apart. 'Back to school,' he told Humphrys, gleefully. I reckon Humphrys will be spoiling for a fight the next time DC goes on.

Wednesday 4 May

DC ushered me into the bathroom earlier than usual this morning for a private chat. I have to admit I feared the worst, because the number of rat sightings has been on the rise lately, just like the jobless figures and the amount of patients on the NHS waiting list, so I sat on the edge of the bath nervously and waited for the boss to lock the door.

He paused for dramatic effect while I sweated silently next to the shower curtain.

'I've decided to turn you into a spud,' he said, reaching for his razor.

'Do what?' I asked. 'They used to burn people at the stake for trying stunts like that.'

'No, no, no. Not a spud – a Spad. It's short for special advisor. I want to make you a Spad.'

'Oh, right,' I said.

'Let me explain,' the boss said patiently.

Ever since Andy Coulson had resigned, DC continued, he'd been worried that there was no one at No 10 who understood where the average punter was coming from, someone like Coulson who was born in an average sort of place and went to an average sort of school.

'Someone with a blue-collar background,' he said. 'I mean Andy didn't even go to university!'

'Well, I've got a blue collar,' I said, 'but I'm not sure I understand all this political stuff. Not yet.'

'Don't worry about all that, old chap,' he said. 'You just need to tell me what you think of some of the policies we're proposing, just like you do on mornings like this when I'm shaving and you're sat on the edge of the bath.'

DC said he valued my 'unique perspective'. He said my new job title was just a way of 'formalizing a role I already performed unofficially'. He said the coalition government had to represent the many, not the few, if it was going to be a success. I said I thought I'd heard that somewhere before.

'It sounds like you want me to be the token working-class bloke at a very posh party,' I said.

'Not *at* the very posh party so much as *in* the very posh party,' DC said, and he leaned against the wall looking pleased with himself.

Sometimes that bloke is too clever by half.

Thursday 5 May

Most of the election results are in and there's no overall winner – just like the last time we held a big vote a year or so ago.

Labour won the by-election, but Boy George called it a pyrrhic victory for young Ed: he gained Leicester South, but lost the whole of Scotland!

DC's lot did badly north of the border too, and so did the Lib Dems. In fact the only real winners up there were the Scottish Nationalists, who had what even George conceded was a remarkable night, and they are determined to have a vote on independence in a few years' time.

DC hates the whole idea. He has already asked that fruitcake Hilton to make sure every policy initiative announced by ministers over the coming weeks refers to 'Great Britain'. He thinks that will remind everyone we're still one country. The cabinet have been told to parachute some patriotic phrases into their speeches for good measure.

I bet Ted and Harold a tenner this morning that we'll be flying the Union Jack over Downing Street before the year is out.

DC and his mate Steve are still banging on about how all that flag-waving last week can be harnessed to improve the national mood, but I told DC today nothing short of winning the Eurovision Song Contest could recapture Friday's atmosphere.

If the boys from Blue could pull that off it really would nudge Hilton's 'National Happiness Index' up a few notches.

But it'd be the biggest split since the Spice Girls broke up if Scotland went its own way.

'Mind you,' DC mused this evening, 'there are seventy-odd Labour MPs up there, so if the Scots did vote for independence there would be a silver lining for the rest of us.'

'What would that be?' I asked.

'We'd never have another Labour government again!'

'Sounds like a tartan lining then?' I told DC.

'Hmmm ... I must make a note of that,' he said, reaching for a pen.

Friday 6 May

I don't reckon Downing Street has seen anything like it since those boozed-up England cricketers were invited in by Tony Blair all those years ago.

DC burst out of the flat this morning and walked straight past the lift, glass of champagne in hand. 'I'm king of the world!' he shouted. 'Master of all I survey! Lord of the manor!'

Then he burst into song – 'I'm the leader of the gang, I am' – and slid down the banister to the bottom of the spiral staircase.

'Don't sing that one in public, boss,' I warned him. 'Gary Glitter's not exactly good for PR these days.'

'Oh, golly, Larry, you're right there,' DC said. 'I'd forgotten about that.'

I don't think he'd even been to bed. As the final results had come in overnight, it became clear Dave had done better than anyone expected. The Tefal-headed number-crunchers on the BBC reckoned the Tories would lose local councils because voters are pretty cheesed off, but in the end they actually won a few, and the AV idea was chucked out an' all.

So Dave scored two victories, while the Lib Dems had to endure another couple of crushing defeats. No wonder DC was rolling around No 10 like a tipsy toff at the last night of the Proms.

I saw Nicky coming down the hallway. DC wiped

his brow, adjusted his tie and tucked his shirt back in, trying hard not to look like he'd been celebrating too hard.

I legged it. I could tell from the look on Nicky's face that he was going to give the first thing he saw a good shoeing – if the Philippe Starck vase next to the pile of *Good Housekeeping* magazines didn't get it, then I would.

Saturday 7 May

Nick Clegg played DC at tennis today. DC won. I think Nicky could handle the result (he's used to losing, after all) but not the manner of the defeat. Boy George, who'd volunteered to be the ballboy, said the boss glided around the court effortlessly, and that's what infuriated Nicky. The thing is, DC never seems to try, even when the rest of us are flapping about like backbenchers trying to catch the Speaker's eye. Perhaps that's just the Eton way.

Sunday 8 May

Boy George was up at Chequers for lunch. He and DC do like to have these cosy little private chats from time to time.

Now that I'm a Spad I get invited along too, occasionally; DC barely even mentions the rats anymore. They will be out of sight soon enough in any case, and hopefully out of my fur for ever.

I couldn't help noticing that a few of the Sunday papers ran stories about Chris Huhne, the guy who kicked off in Cabinet – stories which Olly would normally describe as 'unhelpful'. 'Top minister quizzed over driving ban' the *Sunday Times* reported on its front page.

Huhne is being accused of asking someone else to take his speeding points. He denies it, but Boy George reckons this one could run and run and I can't help thinking none of this would have happened if Huhne had kept his gob shut in Cabinet the other week.

DC was nervous because a scribbler from the *Sun* is coming to No 10 tomorrow to interview him and he's let his subscription lapse.

'I'm a bit out of touch,' he told me. 'What should I say I've been up to?'

'Tell them you've been thinking about offering Keeley from Streatham a government post,' I said, pointing at Page 3 of the paper.

The blurb printed next to the girl in the bikini bottoms read: '23-year-old Keeley from south London is worried about the budget deficit. "Government cuts are tough on everyone," she says. "But they are a price worth paying in order to protect the UK's triple A credit rating."

'Hmm,' said DC. 'She's so worried she's even forgotten to put her clothes on.'

He folded the paper away.

'I don't think so, Larry. I realize it would show I've got a sense of fun, but there are limits. I am the Prime Minister, after all.'

'OK DC, why don't you and Mrs C offer to do a photo story for "Dear Deirdre", the agony aunt column?' I said. '"My wife wants to redecorate our flat, but I can't afford it. Should I risk using taxpayers' money – or tell her to trim the budget by going to B&Q?"'

'Now you're just being silly,' he snapped. 'Anyway, I don't need your advice. I know exactly how to get that lot on side: I'll tell them I went to a pub. Bingo!'

Monday 9 May

It's exactly a year since DC became Prime Minister, and Mrs C started to draw up plans for her expensive refurbishment project upstairs.

I've already learned there's only one way to mark an anniversary around here – invite the *Sun* into Downing Street for an exclusive interview.

DC had a meeting with his most senior cabinet ministers at 9 a.m. to chat about that Gaddafi geezer again, which was scheduled to last an hour and a half, but it was cut short to make time for the *Sun*.

The *Sun* is the paper read by 'our boys', after all, and it's difficult to fight a war without the press on your side.

I could count the number of people who are invited upstairs to DC's pad on the toes of one paw, but I saw the *Sun* journalist step into the lift and head up to the flat – I hope he knows he's being given special treatment.

DC was babysitting tonight while Sam Cam went out, so I sat with him watching *Newsnight*. He fell asleep just after 11 p.m. with a copy of a book in his hand called *The Seven Habits of Highly Effective Prime Ministers*. The walls in the open-plan living room next to the kitchen are lined with reading material. There are old editions of *Who's Who*, back-copies of the *New Statesman* with the pages torn out and every edition of the Argos catalogue from 1993 to the present day (OK, so I made the Argos bit up; but there are a few Boden catalogues scattered around the place). I flicked through a copy of Hans Frei's *Beginner's Guide to Speaking without Notes* and then ended up burying my whiskers in one of Sam Cam's books: *Self-Development in a New Age* by M. Power. What are you doing? I thought to myself when I turned to a chapter called 'Inner Bliss'. This is for losers. I bet Nicky's read all her stuff.

Tuesday 10 May

I decided to pay Ted and Harold a visit to thank them for helping me find the rats' hangout and saving my job in the process. There was a copy of the *Sun* lying next to the monitor and Ted read DC's interview out to me. They'd used DC's line about the boozer. 'I do live in a glass bowl, but I try to get out of it as often as possible,' the boss was quoted as saying. 'Yesterday the Chancellor came for lunch at Chequers, so we went for a walk and ended up in a pub. I'm pleased to say he bought the round.' Do the punters really fall for this stuff?

We were laughing about the old flannel the boss comes out with when the security boys let slip they'd made a shocking discovery last week. It turns out the red-haired kid from IT I'd clocked in the No 10 car park wasn't from IT at all. It was Prince Harry. He was caught on CCTV trying to flog tickets to the royal wedding to the Whitehall Spads – well, I suppose their bosses were desperate to get hold of invitations – only Prince Charles got tipped off and put a stop to it. He barred young Harry from going to Boujis for a week as punishment. The things that go on in this place have to be seen to be believed.

Wednesday 11 May

The saucy scouse Tory MP Nadine Dorries is banging on about how girls should be taught to say 'no' to sex. She isn't part of the awkward squad, as such, but you can tell DC thinks she's one DVD short of a box set.

'Do you think we should get Pickles to have a word with her?' Boy George asked today.

Eric Pickles is a burly bloke the boys send around occasionally to take a chunk out of MPs who step out of line, although his bark is worse than his bite, in my experience.

'Best ignore her,' the boss said. 'She talks more nonsense than John Galliano after two bottles of Fleurie.'

Thursday 12 May

DC had Jenson Button and Lewis Hamilton in today to launch a campaign for road safety. It's amazing what initiatives DC will dream up as an excuse to meet his heroes. There was Spacey, of course, and Elton John is rumoured to be coming in next week. I imagine he's already asked Hilton to start working on a National Vegetarian Week so he can invite Morrissey over for a nut roast. But I'm not sure Hamilton is the right man to persuade people to drive sensibly. Bring back Tufty the Squirrel. I'd have had him for breakfast.

Friday 13 May

The government has been getting a hard time over the amount of expensive wine it serves at receptions. Apparently the Foreign Office are the worst offenders, but I think we should cut them some slack: those embassies have to throw a few decent parties to keep in with the right people, and you can't very well serve pints of John Smith's and Spitfire to the Italian ambassador. One of DC's junior ministers announced the results of a review today: 'We will conduct targeted sales of high-value stock in order to pay for future purchases,' he told the Commons. 'Oh dear, darling,' Sam Cam said. 'Perhaps we shouldn't have opened that crate of Château Latour.'

Saturday 14 May

Kate and Wills are sunning themselves on a private island in the Seychelles, if the scribblers are to be believed. Now, as I've said before, I'm no republican, but if they had an 'austerity wedding' couldn't they have had an 'austerity honeymoon' an' all? I hear Center Parcs has got some good offers on at this time of the year.

The happy couple don't even have to leave Britain if it's sun they're after: according to the *Daily Express*, the heatwave is going to last for ages, with 90° temperatures every day this month. They're already talking about a hosepipe ban in the south-east, and I'm all in favour. I spend far more time than I like to admit dodging those sprinklers in the No 10 Rose Garden.

Sunday 15 May

'The Dude' is about to ride into town. President Obama rocks up in the UK next week, and the flags are already being taken out of storage. It's going to be quite a show, I reckon.

I was hiding out in Sam's knickers drawer this evening, catching some sleep, when I heard DC raving about what a PR coup the whole trip will be.

'Olly's set up some cracking photo ops,' he told Mrs C. 'We're going to have a barbecue in the Rose Garden and visit a local school together.'

'You always did want to hang out with the cool kids,' she said.

'I suppose that's why I married you,' DC replied, smiling.

'Anyway, never mind that,' Sam said. 'Have you heard the big news? Dannii Minogue's been kicked off *The X Factor*.'

'Blimey,' DC said. 'I'll call Cowell later and ask him what happened.'

Sam strode over towards my side of the room. I could hear her footsteps getting louder as she approached, and then she opened the top drawer and let out a scream.

'That cat's got to go!' she shouted.

I ran out of the room with a Stars and Stripes camisole over my head, feeling like a bit of a wally. This cat doesn't do drag.

Still, at least Mrs C is entering into the spirit of things. I wonder if DC will invest in some Uncle Sam underpants.

Monday 16 May

Elton John was in today.

There aren't many people I'm impressed by, but I've always been a big fan of the 'Rocket Man', so I tried to get a look at him up close. The security men know me well enough by now to realize when I'm up to something, so I made sure I followed Elton and his fixer down the corridor at a safe distance.

They were shown into DC's office through the Cabinet Room next door, and when the doors swung open to the boss's study I walked in with them, picking a spot on the carpet next to the arm of one of the sofas and lying low where I couldn't be seen.

Elton turned to look at the paintings dotted around the Den. I'd never noticed them before but I suppose they do look quite impressive.

'Lovely collection,' he said. 'Did you select these pieces?'

'Oh no,' DC replied, laughing. 'They were all left by Gordon.'

Then the two of them got down to business. Elton was in to talk about his AIDS foundation, and DC promised he'd do what he could. Andrew Mitchell, the bloke who decides who gets how much of our overseas aid money, was sat in the meeting as well.

He's an unassuming sort of bloke with a shock of floppy grey hair, but he's another one that's tipped for promotion. Jeremy Heywood, DC's top civil servant, told me once he will probably end up doing Jeremy Hunt's job when Hunt gets a bigger posting.

They chatted about what Elton needed from the government and the meeting wrapped up early.

As his guests got up to leave, DC stood aside and gestured towards the door.

'I've always loved "Piano Man",' he said, for no other reason than to fill an awkward silence.

The temperature in the room plummeted.

'Er, I think that was Billy Joel,' Mitchell said, eventually.

You should have seen Mrs C's face when she heard.

Tuesday 17 May

'I must say, the Queen is having an *annus mirabilis*,' DC said today in front of the shaving mirror.

'Sounds painful,' I replied.

DC winced. It turns out he was talking about what a good year HRH is having. First there was the royal wedding, and now she's going down a storm in Ireland, which isn't a place where she's guaranteed a good reception.

Ireland is one of the few countries that's even more cash-strapped than we are, along with Greece, Portugal and Spain. I suppose that should feel like a consolation of sorts, but then all those Mediterranean places have hot weather and good grub to make up for it. If you're going to be broke, you may as well be warm. Take it from someone who knows.

Even Boy George is worried about the state of the public finances. I'm sure I saw a few grey hairs on his head the other day, although that might be a look he's happy to cultivate given that he's always trying to come across as older then he actually is.

He was having a bit of a ding-dong with DC about it this morning, telling him we had to cut even faster and save even more.

'We should have told the Palace to find some sponsors for that wedding,' he said at one point. 'We could have made a killing. Or at the very least raised enough cash to pay for the bloody thing.'

'I suppose McDonald's could have done the catering,' DC responded, laughing, but I don't think Boy George was joking.

'Well, if it's good enough for the Olympics,' he said.

Wednesday 18 May

Sometimes it feels like DC's the only one in this place with a sure touch, and I can't help wondering if that's the way he likes it.

The latest Cabinet Minister to get himself in a spot of bother is Ken Clarke, the old-timer with the crumpled suits and the Hush Puppies. He went on the BBC to talk about the government's plan to reduce prison sentences and ended up sticking his neck out – so now his head's on the block. It won't be long before the papers start banging on about reshuffles, only there are so many people who could be up for the chop, DC could end up with sore arms from swinging the axe.

Huhne is in deep trouble over this speeding lark, Spelman's been living on borrowed time since the forest fiasco and Lansley's in intensive care. Hague has lost his mojo, the ballroom dancer nearly waltzed off the dancefloor after he'd 'declared war' on Gramps, and Michael Gove, the Scotsman at the Education Department, has had more cock-ups on the job than a randy student at teacher-training college. What a shower.

If DC wasn't on such good terms with the press, he'd have had to wave goodbye to at least four ministers by now. Luckily for him he's with Wills and Kate on this one – the boss is still in his honeymoon period.

As it is, he's only lost Andy Coulson – and I'm proving to be a pretty good stand-in for him.

Thursday 19 May

I heard DC giving someone a dressing down in the Cabinet Room this morning, which is unusual because Dave is rarely in there. He uses it to intimidate ministers who slip up from time to time – it's a bit like being called in to the headmaster's study – but it's something of a last resort; a bit like getting the cane out.

Poor old Ken Clarke, I thought. He won't be enjoying getting a rollicking from a bloke who's young enough to be his son.

They say curiosity killed the cat, so I pegged it downstairs, past my blanket and the scratching post with Milimouse hanging from it, and made my way to the porch that sits on the other side of those patio doors at the back of the Cabinet Room to get a better view.

Gawping through the gap in the door, I could make out two sets of shoes, but then I clocked that both pairs were black, shiny leather. There wasn't a Hush Puppy in sight.

It was Clarke's underling at the Ministry of Justice, Crispin Blunt, who was being read the riot act by DC.

He was the one who first brought up all this sentencing business, and Clarke had been forced to defend what his junior partner had said when he did the rounds of the radio and TV studios – or so the boss seemed to imply.

That sounds harsh on Blunt, but then he's got form: he said last year that prisoners should be allowed to throw parties in jail, which didn't exactly endear him to DC. Or the group known as 'middle England'. It sounds like Blunt's been none too sharp.

By the way, I do hope Crispin Blunt and Jeremy Hunt are never invited to appear on the *Today* programme together.

Friday 20 May

A banker called Fred has been outed as one of the bad boys who've been trying to stop the papers writing about his home life.

A load of rich and famous types have been going to the high court to get 'super-injunctions' which stop the press from telling their readers who has been getting up to what, where and when. To be truthful, I don't know why you lot are so bashful about your nocturnal activities. It's not something us felines can relate to. You must have heard the sound of us cats going about our business outside, after all, screeching and caterwauling. But then again, I suppose none of you lot much fancy cleaning your hind-quarters in full public view like we do. Each to their own, as they say. But since DC's always trying to ingratiate himself with those powerful editors, he's come down on their side of the fence, as per usual.

DC reckons we're all scribblers now. Any of us can go on Twitter and publish whatever we like. I had a butcher's today and noticed that at least a half-dozen people have set up Twitter accounts pretending to be the Downing Street cat – which is a right liberty! I've a reputation to protect. I'm working on how I could take out a super-injunction against my imposters. I don't know what the penalty is for impersonating a cat these days but I'd be tempted to settle it the old-fashioned way if I got my claws into them. There's only one Larry and he's got his paws well under the table. They'd all do well to scarper once I've published my diary.

Saturday 21 May

D-day. I was slightly concerned the rats might be having second thoughts about the wisdom of storming the Palace, so I emailed King Rat a link to a story in this morning's *Daily Mirror*, just to give the guys the extra encouragement they might need. DC's uncle Sir William Dugdale had said 'the working classes prefer to be led by a Duke', which is guaranteed to get right up their pointy little noses.

I did a bit of digging and it turns out Dugdale is a former chairman of Aston Villa. So that's why DC supports the Villa – his uncle used to run the club.

The rats were suitably unimpressed, but I needn't have worried about them. They are looking forward to causing a bit of mayhem. I'm just glad it'll be those corgis that will have to pick up the pieces from now on instead of me – provided everything goes to plan, of course.

I'd thought long and hard before selecting the date. The rats wanted to move on the day before the wedding, when the Palace staff would have been preoccupied with preparations for the big day, but I vetoed that on the grounds there would have been far too many coppers crawling around the place.

If we were going to pull this off, I told them, we had to strike after the wedding, but before the Obama state visit, when Downing Street and the Palace would both be busy finalizing the arrangements for the second big event of the spring. We settled on the 21st because it was still a few days before the CIA roll into town to sweep the Palace (I know because I saw an email about it next to the recycling bin on the ground floor – they really should make better use of those shredders George invested in).

There were a few nerves jangling and noses twitching when we assembled at 2 a.m. in the basement. Harold and Ted had agreed to turn the CCTV cameras off in the canteen for two minutes, which gave us just enough time to prize the specials board away from the wall to expose the small hole the rats have been digging for weeks. Operation Infestation was underway.

I had to accompany them into the sewage system and escort them through the network of pipes at King Rat's insistence. I don't think he trusts me, so having me down there with them made him feel slightly more comfortable. I'm no grass, although I suppose he's not to know that, but I didn't relish having to crawl through mile upon mile of Victorian tunnels to prove it. I shudder at the memory of those two hours but I will spare you the details. Let's just say it was more *Shawshank Redemption* than *Escape to Victory*.

By the time we finally reached our destination, crawling out in the State Dining Room, it was the early hours of Sunday morning and the servants were clearing away the breakfast table.

HRH must have had visitors, because she'd got her best china out, and it looked like they'd had a bit of a blow-out. There were piles of Duchy Originals biscuits next to the leftover bacon and eggs and half-eaten toast.

'Am I losing it?' one footman said to another. 'Or was there a piece of Edam on that side plate a second ago?'

I turned around and King Rat had scarpered, cheese in gob, with the rest of them not far behind him, carrying as many croissants and Danish pastries as they could manage.

I tell you what: the firm aren't going to know what's hit them.

I got to the bottom of what happened to DC's old mobile while we were body-boarding through the brown stuff. 'Come on, boys,' I said. 'What's the story?'

There was some hesitation and a fair amount of stalling, but I got it out of them in the end. King Rat had swiped the mobile from under Harold and Ted's noses, just as I suspected. When he realised it was still operational, he flogged it to some dodgy security bloke as a middle man. That explains the scene I witnessed on smokers' corner on the hottest day of the year.

With Sam Cam still leaving voicemails on DC's old phone, it wasn't long before the papers were using it to find out their movements ahead of time. I hate to think what would have happened if Mrs C had left any intimate messages for the boss. His inside leg measurements could have been plastered all over the papers by now!

Sunday 22 May

I woke up this morning and stretched, then wandered through to the Den. DC was sat there in his pyjamas in front of the telly, munching his way through a bowl of All-Bran.

I could see the TV was tuned to BBC One, for a

change, because the presenter who was blathering away on screen was the same bloke who interviewed the boss in the White Room on the first floor at Downing Street a few days after I first arrived.

'Don't let Gramps see you watching the BBC,' I said as I walked into the room.

'Shhhh,' DC said, and turned the volume up.

It was only when I jumped on to his lap that I saw Sam was on the other side, picking dried cranberries from the palm of her hand and popping them, one by one, into her mouth.

I've never seen Sam show an interest in politics before, but when I glanced back at the TV the penny dropped. Obama was being interviewed from the splendour of the diplomats' room at the White House, a spacious, elaborately decorated room with high ceilings which overlooks the perfectly manicured lawn.

Mrs C was clearly impressed. She's got a pretty good eye for these things. 'I know we've got a new kitchen, but this place could still do with a bit of an extreme home makeover,' she said.

DC sighed. 'We've spent about half-a-million quid doing Downing Street up since we arrived,' he said.

'Have we? Even so, the White House makes Downing Street look like a two-up two-down.'

'Well, it's a good job the Obamas are staying at the Palace then,' DC said, and he turned the volume up still louder.

It's not easy trying to keep up with the Obamas.

203

Monday 23 May

I wasn't the only scally in Downing Street today. DC invited a homeless chap into No 10. The London *Evening Standard* has been running a campaign to raise money for people who live on the streets and the boss was doing his bit. This geezer is a bit down on his luck, and I could see by the look on his face how much it meant to him to be sat chatting to DC around the Cabinet table. Believe me, I know exactly how he felt.

It already feels like a lifetime ago, but I remember how happy I was to be brought in from the cold in February, when the last of the winter snow had only just melted away. I must have spent hours warming my backside on that photocopier in the events room that first week.

I realized later why the homeless guy had been invited in. DC made another BS speech tonight all about loving thy neighbour.

'He wants to watch it,' I told Olly this evening. 'Boy George might get the wrong idea.'

So Olly agreed to let the homeless geezer through the big black door today because he knew DC was delivering his touchy-feely patter tonight – he's getting the hang of these photo opportunities.

No one was paying much attention to what DC said, of course, because Obama is in Ireland en route to the UK tonight, twelve hours sooner than planned.

We have the Icelandic ash cloud to thank for his early arrival. The Dude was in Dublin this afternoon, sipping a pint of Guinness, charming the locals and wining louder cheers than the Queen.

He certainly upstaged HRH and Prince Philip, who only left Ireland on Friday. The Dude is like a rock star about to begin a sold-out European tour. I don't think DC much likes the idea of being the warm-up act, but part of him is just happy to be on the same bill.

Tuesday 24 May

I was so nervous about the Dude's visit to No 10 I could barely sleep last night. Will Obama meet me? Has anyone briefed him about me? Will he sit in the Larry chair? One of the teenage helpers told me last night he bought a 'Portuguese water dog' for his two teenage girls. You don't see too many of those in Battersea, so I've no idea what kind of mutt that is. But it's marked him out as a dog-lover, which means he might be a cat-hater. Oh no!

Then I got a grip of myself and thought about what my old man might have said: 'He isn't sitting there on Air Force One worrying about meeting you, so why are you so worried about meeting him?'

I still woke up with butterflies in my stomach, and I swear DC's hand was just a little unsteady when he shaved in the bathroom mirror this morning, but then I remembered the rats aren't around anymore, so at least they couldn't cause any bother.

Only then everyone started talking about 'the beast'. At first I thought they were being mean about Eric Pickles, but he's pretty popular at this place, so the more they mentioned it the more worried I became.

One of the events girls shouted: 'The beast is on its way.' Then thirty seconds later one of the teenage helpers said: 'It's coming down The Mall!' It was like a nightmare from my kittenhood, or a badly financed horror film.

By the time the beast was spotted on Whitehall I was beside myself, and when one of the garden girls shouted out, 'The beast is here!' I was cowering behind the Obama chair.

Then Harriet told me they were talking about the Dude's car – a pimped-up, armour-plated limo. It's a beast of a machine, or so she said, with its own oxygen supply, a panic button and smoked windows. I felt like a right muppet.

I watched through the window as the Dude's entourage clambered out. Everyone pretended to be busy when he walked through that big black door.

I was too jumpy to stick around, and I didn't have the energy to push through all those legs to get a sighting, so I made myself scarce while Obama met with DC. He'll be back again tomorrow so I can get a closer look then.

After an hour or so, the Dude was back in the beast and off to the Palace for a state banquet hosted by the Queen and Prince Philip. I expect those rats had been hiding under one of the enormous tables in the State Dining Room since the early evening to make sure they caught a glimpse of the Dude too.

Wednesday 25 May

The Dude addressed both Houses of Parliament today. Apparently that was a first. I wasn't there to see it but I could hear the helicopters circling overhead as he made his way to Westminster Hall, where Tony Blair and Gordon Brown were waiting for him in prime spots at the front of the building.

Was it my imagination, or did both of them look quite pleased to be there? They may have missed out on the wedding last month, but this was a far more historic occasion, after all.

John Major was there too, standing shoulder to shoulder with his successors. They'd invited all the ex-Prime Ministers, and only dear old Mrs T couldn't make it.

Young Ed Miliband was stuck next to his MPs and their partners a few rows back, which made him look like a bit-part player if you ask me. But at least he got a private chat with the Dude at the Palace last night before the big banquet. It's a lot more than Nicky got.

Before Obama's big speech he was in at our gaff again, pressing the flesh and charming the garden girls. When he posed outside that big front door I managed to sneak out so I could take in the moment.

I got the shock of my life when I saw the number of snappers outside. There were so many of them they had to stand on stepladders so they could get a proper shot.

Sam Cam showed Mrs Dude around her new kitchen. It's her pride and joy that place. The White House staff even took a few pictures of the First Lady and Mrs C sitting on that cornflower-coloured sofa.

Then it was time for the barbecue DC was so excited about. It went off without a hitch – no flame-grilled chicken wings burnt to a crisp, and no unfortunate accidents with the firelighters.

Michelle and Sam served salad to ex-servicemen, and the Dude did the bangers and burgers along with DC.

Olly must have been well chuffed with the shots of the two of them that were on the news tonight: there was no rain, and even the wind couldn't ruin the occasion.

It was strange to watch the Dude and his missus stroll around in the Rose Garden – the part of this place I've got to know best – surrounded by black-suited security men wearing earpieces and sunglasses. I was worried Nicky would sneak out there and try to look cool by offering Obama one of his cigarettes, but DC had told me that he'd locked him in his room for the duration of the visit. It was only afterwards I found out that Nicky did meet Barack after all.

I would have found that hard to deal with were it not for the fact that I met him too. Suddenly and without warning, Obama was ushered into the side-room where I was chomping away on some burger gristle left over from the barbecue.

He strolled into the room with a couple of his burly FBI men, who arrived before he did, looking around the room anxiously from behind their jet-black shades.

There was a photographer standing ready to take a few shots, of course.

Sometimes I can't help thinking I was hired for PR purposes rather than to catch those rats. I guess those papers need something to fill their pages with, but recently it's all too often been me. It's slightly unnerving but I think I rose to the occasion, tail fluffed up and whiskers clean.

Obama was beaming, despite the fact he hasn't had too much to smile about recently. He's getting a right kicking in the polls back at home, according to DC, who seemed to be smiling as he told me about it. Perhaps it was just a trick of the light, because he's been matey as anything with him on this trip. But I guess it's not just an ocean that separates them – he and Obama are supposed to be on opposites sides of the political divide, after all.

The snapper snapped away as the Dude stroked me half-heartedly, but then I noticed with a shock that he was wearing a short-sleeved shirt. Has any man ever looked the part in a short-sleeved work shirt? I'm sorry, but even the Dude couldn't pull that one off. He's the First Man when all is said and done, and although it may have been unseasonably sweltering today, I'd far rather have seen him roll his sleeves up. Still, history won't judge him on his sartorial slip-ups, and even the boss knows he can't compete with Obama. No one comes close to the Dude. That's why he's the Dude.

After Obama and his posse had left I clambered out of my basket and walked on to the terrace at the back of No 10, picturing the scene a few hours earlier when the soldiers mingled with the Dude and the First Lady. And then it hit me.

I'm the First Cat. The Top Cat. The King of the Pile. I'm where I always dreamed of being but never thought I'd end up. The rats are gone, at least for now, and I'm still here, hopefully for a long time to come.

I turned to go back indoors and then I remembered what my old nan used to say on days like this: 'Turned out nice again.'

Friday 15 July – postscript

I stopped penning my diary after 100 days. Self-discipline's never been my strong point and, in any case, I'd reached the last page of my little Smythson notebook. I did look into buying another one, but it would have cost me fifteen notes! No wonder Sam Cam's not short of a few bob. Even that Basildon Bond stuff my old mum used to keep in her top drawer cost well under a fiver, if memory serves, so it goes to show how these posh types throw their money around for the designer labels. Someone's making a nice mark-up there.

Sam and DC are doing OK, even if the yoga DVDs she's doing are causing the odd argument or two. But it feels like No 10 has been turned upside down in the few short weeks since the royal wedding and the Dude's visit.

We don't see much of that flame-haired diva Rebekah Brooks for a start, and Gramps is notable by his absence. All that phone-hacking stuff turned into a proper ding-dong, with top Old Bill resigning and all sorts. The real rats may have been turfed out of No 10, but the truth is it's some of those hacks that belong in the sewer. Rebekah had to resign and Gramps shut down one of his papers. I'm sure the champagne corks are still popping round at Ryan Giggs's place, but where am I going to get all the football gossip from now that the new season has started?

I've never seen DC looking as flustered as when there were new revelations every day about just how low our friends in the press had sunk. He barely even stopped to acknowledge me when we passed one another on the stairs the day the *News of the World* closed down. I know the boss is ruthless, but even he must have felt a twinge of guilt when he said Rebekah should resign. After all, he was a guest of hers only last month, sipping champagne and eating oysters at some posh joint in Kensington with Rupert and his pup James.

Gramps was even hauled up before Parliament and given a right going over, and near the end of his two-hour cross-examination, some joker managed to stick a foam pie in his boat race. You should have seen his missus Wendi, a willowy-looking Chinese beauty, plant a left hook on the bloke that attacked her fella. They say Nicky's bird Miriam is a feisty one, but Wendi can handle herself alright!

Everyone's been having a go – Paxo has been revelling in it and even floppy-haired fop and rom-com heartthrob Hugh Grant has been sticking it to Gramps and coming over all 'man of the people'. I didn't know he had it in him. Of course Ed Miliband's seized on the story with triumphant glee and has become the Milimouse that Roared.

No one talks that fondly about Andy Coulson any more – DC has suddenly started reminding everyone it was Boy George's idea to hire him in the first place.

And me? Well, I did come across a rogue rodent the

other week, but I cornered him and we did a deal. He agreed to play dead for a few minutes while I gave him directions to the Palace then took the credit for the catch. It's what I call the 'diplomatic solution'. I've been watching those old *Minder* reruns on ITV4 and learning a few tips from Arthur Daley. Everyone has a price at the end of the day and I'm sure those hacks would agree. After all, there's nothing new under the *Sun*, is there?

King Rat sent word from the Palace that they've got a nice little set-up round the back of the kitchens. Apparently the grub over there is 'reet proper posh' but they're staying out of the way of Her Majesty. They've heard what she's like when she gets her hands on a pheasant, so they don't fancy their chances and are keeping well clear of both her and her corgis.

Harriet's still being good to me and Downing Street is finally starting to feel like the home I never had. So I'm right as rain, tickety-boo – never better. In fact, I'm as happy as Larry.